ALLEGRA ETHERIDGE

Allegra Etheridge is the Director of a Coaching Psychology and Workplace Mediation company. She's dedicated to improving working lives and supporting clients to achieve positive change. She has a degree in English and Psychology and two postgraduate qualifications in Publishing and Human Resource Management.

As well as the four Workbooks in the *Coaching Psychology Series*, she has written two books of metaphors for hypnotherapists. These are set texts for hypnotherapy training courses in the UK and elsewhere. She has a Diploma in Solution Focused Hypnotherapy.

Allegra lives in Gloucestershire, UK, with her husband Peter and their cats.

Increasing
Empowerment

Workbook

Allegra Etheridge

First published 2023

British Library Cataloguing-in-publication data

A catalogue entry for this book is available from the British Library

ISBN: 978-1-7393903-0-3 (printed version)

ISBN: 978-1-7393903-1-0 (ebook version)

Published by Write-Film-Edit, Gloucestershire

Designed by Chloe Tyler

Edited by Dee Holley

Printed and bound by Mixam, 6 Hercules Way, Watford, Hertfordshire, WD25 7GS UK

This book is produced using recycled paper and is earth-friendly

Other Books by the Author

Increasing Inner Confidence Workbook

Managing Emotions Workbook: Including Stress and Anger

Managing Self-Consciousness Workbook

Effective Metaphors for Children: A Resource for Therapists, Parents and Teachers

Effective Metaphors for Hypnotherapy, with Tayma Wallbridge

Disclaimer

The author of this work has made every effort to ensure that the information contained in this Workbook is accurate at the time of publication. Medical and psychological knowledge is constantly changing, and the application of the Workbooks depends on many situational and personal factors.

It's recommended that readers seek support from a qualified specialist for individual psychological advice, where necessary. This book should not be used as an alternative to specialist medical advice for mental health conditions.

The author is not responsible for any errors or omissions in the text, which is provided in good faith.

This book is dedicated to Muriel

Contents

📖 Introduction

Welcome to the **Coaching Psychology Series.** Coaching Psychology is a branch of coaching which uses psychological theory to enhance work with clients.

There are four Workbooks in this Series which can be used as tools to support individual self-development.

The Workbooks take the view that the best foundation to become fulfilled and achieve goals is strong inner confidence, empowered communication and the ability to manage emotions. I've called the mastery of these three areas: the **Stable Response.**

Stable Response

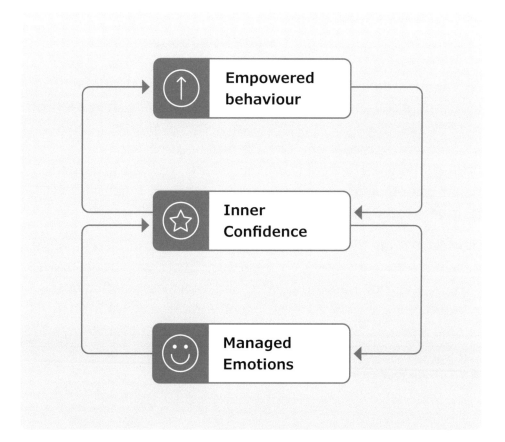

The **Stable Response** shows a positive interaction between empowered behaviour, high inner confidence and emotional management. Here, you function at your best and are positive.

During my coaching psychology and workplace mediation practice, I developed this approach as I found that this was the most effective way to support clients. One of my client groups were doctors in the National Health Service in the UK. With only a short period of time to work with them, I needed a quick diagnostic tool to support their self-awareness and to enable them to create positive change in their lives.

> **Unfortunately, stressors, challenging life events, environmental, health and psychological issues can create instability in one or more areas of the Stable Response.**

One way that this affects the **Stable Response** is for people to exaggerate their behaviour. This may mean that even though their confidence may take a knock, they react by appearing more confident than they feel. I call this **fragile high confidence**. They could also assert themselves over people in the way that they communicate and become 'Alpha' – or more dominant. They could also lose some of their emotional management, such as being angry or stressed. I call this the **Exaggerated Response.**

The second way that stressors and life events can affect people is for them to withdraw. This means that their self-belief takes a knock and they become quieter and show less confidence in their abilities. They can also become more passive in their communication. They may lose some of their emotional management, particularly in areas such as anxiety and self-consciousness.

Exaggerated Response

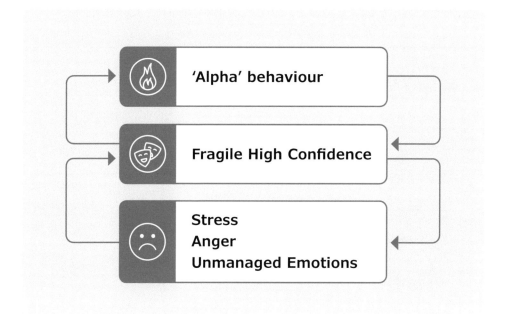

Withdrawn Response

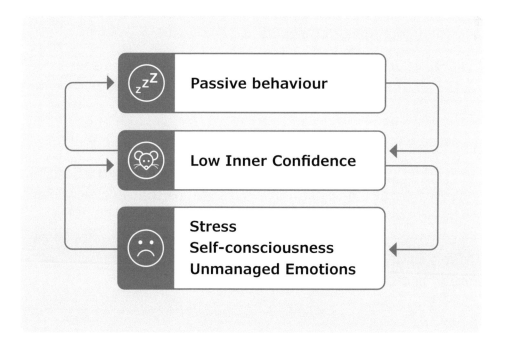

It's possible to be stable in one or two areas but show exaggerated or withdrawn responses in the others. These Workbooks aim to encourage the Stable Response, assisting whichever area is exaggerated or withdrawn.

How the Workbooks Help

The Workbooks in the **Coaching Psychology Series** are:

- **Increasing Inner Confidence Workbook**

- **Increasing Empowerment Workbook**

- **Managing Emotions Workbook: Including Stress and Anger**

- **Managing Self-consciousness Workbook**

They provide a range of practical and flexible strategies for an individualised approach to self-development.

The Workbooks aim to make psychology accessible but also focus on interacting with solutions.

They're deliberately concise and short so that they're something to pick up, think about, and return to at another time.

All the Workbooks have been trialled with clients and have been improved with feedback, to make them as useful as possible.

I've worked with clients from a variety of cultures and where English isn't their first language. This means that I've simplified the language in the Workbooks to increase accessibility. The Flesch Reading Ease score is 64.6 (plain English, which is easily understood by 13-15 year olds). In addition, the font type and spacing is designed to be dyslexia friendly.

The Workbooks complement each other but can be read on their own, or in combination.

For further information for coaches about the Workbooks see page 197.

On a personal note, these Workbooks have been a labour of love for seven years. I hope that as either a client or a coach you find them useful and supportive for your development, future and practice.

Allegra Etheridge

August 2023

If you would like to contact me, I'd be delighted to hear from you:

allegra@write-film-edit.co.uk

Increasing Empowerment

Welcome to your **Increasing Empowerment Workbook**. Congratulations on investing time and energy in you.

This Workbook will provide you with information, strategies and tools to help you to become more empowered in how you communicate and behave.

> **The strategies are split into two sections.** The first section (p 21) will support you if you tend to be overly assertive (or **Alpha**). The second section (p 105) will support you if you tend to be **passive** in your behaviour.
>
> There's an **Empowerment Audit** at the end of the Workbook to measure how you tend to behave. I suggest you have a go at this now to see what you score (see p 191).

Research shows that positive thinking is a potent way to change your life. One of the ways that I encourage you to enhance your empowerment is through positive affirmations. These are short phrases that either feel authentic to you or are aspirational. You'll see these throughout the Workbook. They aim to reinforce positive emotions, thoughts and behaviours.

If you find one that you like, you can repeat it to yourself – either out loud or in your head. Do this five times in a row in the morning when you wake up and five times when you go to bed. This aims to speed up you becoming positively empowered by working with your conscious and subconscious mind.

The other approach I take is through metaphors – there's one for being Alpha and one for being passive in this Workbook. The purpose of including these is to appeal to your subconscious mind about the benefits of empowered behaviour.

Being passive, just like being Alpha is a habitual set of thoughts, feelings and behaviours which you can change with time, motivation and focus.

Definitions

For the purpose of this Workbook, Empowerment is defined as:

Being confident in pursuing your needs, whilst being respectful of the needs of others. When it's necessary, you'll influence others, set boundaries and clearly express your thoughts and feelings. Here, you approach the world in a positive and active way.

For the purpose of this Workbook, Alpha is defined as:

Becoming fixed on having things go your way, believing that to dominate and use tactics is the most effective way to achieve this. Stress can cause this behaviour to become particularly noticeable.

For the purpose of this Workbook, Passivity is defined as:

Being submissive and prioritising the needs of others over your own needs. Passivity is about tending to withdraw when you feel challenged. You find initiating action is challenging.

The **Increasing Inner Confidence Workbook** in the **Coaching Psychology Series** focuses on your relationship with yourself. This Workbook on empowerment focuses on your relationship with others.

Psychology of Empowerment

There are three ways to approach being empowered, namely:

1 Alpha **2** Passive **3** Empowered

You'll be capable of all these approaches, depending on the situation you're in or whether you're feeling emotionally overwhelmed. However, you'll tend to generally prefer one approach over another.

There are three areas which have a role to play in empowerment:

1 **Inner confidence:** The quality of the relationship you have with yourself

2 **Honesty:** Your willingness to be honest with yourself and others

3 **Responsibility:** How you approach stepping in to challenging situations

 **Inner Confidence**

The foundation for empowerment is inner confidence.
To act in an empowered way, you need to believe in, and
draw on, that belief in your own abilities. Inner confidence
and empowerment work together in a dynamic way. If you
believe that you're a worthwhile person who has something
to offer, it makes pursuing your needs an easier prospect.

However, you may appear confident to others but have
insecurities, which you may hide. This means that your
confidence is fragile. Or your low confidence may be obvious to
others, and you may clearly doubt yourself and your ability to
communicate effectively. Both of these attitudes to yourself can
undermine your attempts to become empowered with others.

If you feel that confidence may be an issue for you,
considering developing this too via the companion book
Increasing Inner Confidence Workbook in the **Coaching
Psychology Series.**

 **Honesty**

Being honest with others is crucial for empowered behaviour.
Opening up about your needs, goals, emotions and thoughts
will enable you to be much more likely to succeed. Depending
on the situation you're in, this approach can create trust,
rapport and understanding between yourself and the person
you're communicating with.

Opening up is a balancing act which weighs up who you're
with and what you're communicating about. **Empowerment
is giving enough honest information so that the other
person understands you.**

However, it can be challenging to be clear about your needs with others. You may feel vulnerable about doing this - particularly about personal matters. You may avoid communicating about deeper issues because of feelings of pride and self-consciousness.

 Responsibility

Empowered behaviour is asking yourself what's genuinely your responsibility in any given situation. You decide if it's your place to step in and act. Taking responsibility might occur if you see something unjust and feel that you need to say your piece. The empowered approach is about not robbing someone else of their responsibility by stepping in too much or robbing yourself of power by stepping back.

> The challenge if you tend to be Alpha is that you'll step in more than is necessary. You'll find it easier to direct the action and take control.
>
> The challenge if you tend to be passive, is that you'll find it easier to step back and let others make decisions.

Transactional Analysis and Empowerment

It can be useful to categorise communication into three styles. These are behaving like a 'parent,' 'child' or 'adult'. This theory is known as **Transactional Analysis** (Eric Berne). In different circumstances, you may move from one style to another, depending on who you're with.

 Parent-style

There are two types of parent-style behaviour:

1 'critical parent'

2 'nurturing parent'

The critical parent type is where you'll try to dominate others with your judgemental opinions as a critical parent would do to a child. This relates to be Alpha behaviours.

The nurturing parent type is where you're more permissive and protective with others. When using this type, you may be reluctant to be honest or to set boundaries for fear of upset as a parent who indulges their child would be. This relates to being passive.

> If you've experienced either of these types from your parent or caregiver when you were a child, you may now be repeating these behaviours yourself. You may also be doing the opposite, as you may be keen not to show this behaviour, knowing that it wasn't helpful.

 **Child-style**

There are two types of child-style behaviours:

1 'adapted child'

2 'free child'

When you behave like an adapted child, you're less direct and could even be manipulative. You may avoid explaining your thoughts and feelings to others. You may hope to get your own way indirectly. This relates to passive behaviours.

The free child behaviour type is about not wanting to take responsibility. Here, you may avoid thinking about your needs. This means that others may end up making decisions for you. This is another potential passive approach.

 Adult-style

Adult-style behaviour is the foundation for empowerment. When you use this style, you're logical and emotionally intelligent. Adult communication is about listening, being honest but tactful and bravely approaching challenging subjects with calmness.

> **Feeling stressed can make it more challenging to be adult, particularly if the person you're with isn't communicating in an adult style. The challenge is to remain adult as much as possible, no matter what style another person is using or how stressed you feel.**

Misunderstandings about Empowerment

There are some misunderstandings about empowerment in the mainstream. **Unfortunately, some outdated ideas related to assertiveness linger on and have been associated with empowerment.**

The first misunderstanding is about how, by using persistence, you'll get your way. The truth is that empowered behaviour means that you put yourself into a strong position to get your own way, but that you're not guaranteed to get it – particularly if you use persistence.

The second misunderstanding is that being empowered means relying on being frank and direct. This is, in fact, a hallmark of being Alpha.

The third misunderstanding is that empowerment has a formula which tends to be variations of the following:

- Stating your view of what you perceive to be going on

- Using 'I' statements such as: 'I think' and 'I feel'

- Describing how another person's behaviour has negatively affected you

- Stating what you want – which is usually a change in behaviour from the other person

- Repeating what you want if this is challenged

An example of this would be: 'Yesterday you talked over me in our Senior Leaders Meeting, which was my slot. I felt undermined and hurt that you didn't let me speak. In the future, give me the time which is allotted.'

This formula doesn't work in all but the most extreme situations, for the following reasons:

- Apart from being stubborn, it doesn't support with how to continue a conversation in a real-life situation

- It assumes that you've the power to change another person's behaviour, when the only person you can change is yourself

- It can be perceived by the person on the receiving end as confrontational

- It ignores that stepping back can be an empowered act

- It may not be your natural communication style

- It's just about your point of view and doesn't encourage a conversation

That said, with someone who's highly inappropriate or aggressive, who repeatedly ignores your needs and boundaries, this approach could be helpful.

Starting off softly leaves room to gradually become more direct, if necessary, so use the minimum amount of assertion in any given situation. This model uses the maximum amount of assertion as the first port of call. Treat it as the last resort.

Stages of Empowerment

There are six stages to becoming empowered:

1 **Understanding yourself** – who you are – both in terms of strengths and development areas

2 **Defining your needs** – what must be in your life to give it meaning and ultimately happiness

3 **Deciding your wants** – optional things that you'd like to have or what you'd like to happen

4 **Making goals** – turning your needs into practical plans

5 **Pursuing your goals** – showing confidence in trying to achieve your goals, despite setbacks

6 **Setting boundaries** – preventing others from taking too much of your time and energy, so that you can achieve your goals

All of these stages are included in the strategies to become empowered described later in this Workbook.

Benefits of Empowerment

Empowered behaviour has a wide range of potential benefits, including:

- **Accepting yourself** for who you are and being straightforward about that with others

- **Acknowledging your successes** without having to boast

- **Analysing feedback** of your performance or behaviour with curiosity

- Being confident and **clear about pursuing your goals**

- **Being enthusiastic** about what matters to you

- Being **flexible** and willing to adjust your direction in the light of new information

- **Being mature** in the way that you communicate – even if the person you're communicating with isn't behaving in a mature way with you

- Being **persistent over important matters** particularly when you're pressurised to step back, or if you meet barriers

- **Clearly speaking up** when it's important to shed light on a situation, particularly if it's not what others want to hear

- Communicating your needs and thoughts with **honesty and tact**

- Having **clear conversations**, rather than confrontations where negative emotions take over

- **Listening** to other's points of view respectfully, objectively evaluating what they say in light of your own point of view

- **Negotiating** when you feel it's necessary

- Setting **boundaries** with others to protect your time and energy

- Showing **body language** which says to others that you're an equal

- **Showing trust** which aims to bring out the best in others

- **Standing up for your rights** when it matters

- **Staying focused**, despite the pressure of life events and the negative opinions of others

- **Taking responsibility** and stepping up to the mark

- When necessary **being open with others about your feelings**, without perceiving this as a weakness

This can lead to:

- **Avoiding regret** by not repressing your needs
- **Avoiding unresolved issues** in your life by facing and working on them as they arise
- Being **less at risk of conflict**
- Being **less likely to be taken advantage of** by others
- Being **more in control** of the direction your life takes
- **Being your authentic self** in all situations
- Broadening your perspective by **openly considering other views**
- Building strong, **honest relationships**
- Engaging with **reflective thinking** which increases self-development
- Feeling **less overwhelmed**
- Focusing on the future with **clarity**
- **Handling conflict** by stepping-in and having clear conversations when they're needed
- **Prioritising what you care about**
- Setting **helpful boundaries**
- Taking time to **understand others**
- **Taking up opportunities** as they arise

> As you start working on increasing your empowerment, it can be useful to keep referring back to this section, to remind yourself of the purpose of the work that you're doing.

Your Body and Empowerment

A complex mix of physical factors can affect having empowered behaviour. This might be to do with underlying diseases, hormonal imbalance, stress, fatigue and the use of drugs and alcohol. Dementia, Alzheimer's disease and head injuries can also affect your ability to be empowered.

> If you feel that you would benefit from support with any of these issues, then your GP can help.

Specifically related to Alpha behaviour is the hormone testosterone. This can lead to wanting dominance and to be competitive. It's related to the male instinct to protect your turf.

You may also feel a buzz when you get your own way due to the hormone dopamine, which can be released when a risk that you take pays off. This can be connected to a tendency towards Alpha behaviour.

Being Alpha means being on alert to respond and take control. This can cause a release of stress hormones and increase your blood pressure. Over a long period of time, cumulative stress will also eventually take a physical and mental toll.

Mental Health and Empowerment

Some mental health conditions relate to being highly Alpha.

- **Narcissistic Personality Disorder (NPD)** – this is about taking advantage of people who don't have strong boundaries, needing to feel dominant, powerful and having a sense of entitlement

- **Oppositional Defiant Disorder** – this is related to being Alpha and concerns being in a long-standing pattern of angry, irritable and argumentative behaviour

- **Paranoid Personality Disorder** – this is where you believe that other people are out to get you and you've an exaggerated sense of suspicion and mistrust. This can lead to Alpha behaviour

However, if you tend to be Alpha or passive, it doesn't necessarily mean that you've a mental health disorder. Disorders are a long-term inability to alter your behaviour, despite making efforts to do so. This Workbook does not aim to support people with a mental health condition, which would need specialist treatment.

Related Workbooks

The **Coaching Psychology Series** has three other Workbooks which can support increasing empowered behaviour.

They are:

- **Increasing Inner Confidence Workbook** – this is about nurturing a positive relationship with yourself. Self-belief creates a solid foundation for empowerment.

- **Managing Emotions Workbook: Including Stress and Anger** – this is about how to develop emotional control when you're experiencing negative emotions. It focuses on how to manage frustration, which can be related to Alpha behaviour. It also addresses managing stress, which can be an issue if you've either Alpha or passive behaviour.

- **Managing Self-consciousness Workbook** – this provides approaches to support with a fear of social situations. If you tend to be passive, you may also feel self-conscious and challenged by some social situations.

The Workbook now splits into two sections, the first supports if you've a tendency towards Alpha behaviour (p 21-104), the second supports if you've a tendency towards passive behaviour (p 105-190).

 Alpha Behaviour

Alpha Metaphor

> The purpose of this metaphor is to tell a story about being Alpha. This story aims to communicate with your subconscious, rather than conscious mind. Your conscious mind will be engaging with the facts and information about empowerment while your subconscious mind prefers metaphors.
>
> If you're working with a hypnotherapist, this story could be incorporated into a trance session to help support your subconscious mind with being empowered.

At this time, it was hot and dry, and water was expensive and scarce. Neighbouring countries relied on water to irrigate their crops, for the use of their people and animals and, indeed, for everyone's survival.

The Queen of one of the countries was obsessed with getting and storing water. The more she thought about it, the more she plotted about how to get it.

Eventually, she decided to take more water than had been agreed from the river on her border, which she and that neighbouring country both used.

It was initially an incredible success for the Queen. For the first time the Queen and the subjects in her Kingdom had more water than they'd had in living memory. It yielded spectacular results, crops were irrigated, the survival of people and animals in her country seemed secured.

However, before the Queen could enjoy her success, her country was invaded by an army from the neighbouring country whose water had now become incredibly scarce. They were hurt at the betrayal they felt, and they were also incredibly angry.

From this bitterness came years of conflict, leading to pain and suffering.

But the Queen would not back down.

Sometimes it seemed like the war would never end. The Queen felt the pain and was tired and sad. She lost friends, good will and peace.

As time went on, as difficult as it was for the Queen to admit, she had to change because the war had to end.

She met with the King of the neighbouring country by the bank of the disputed river. They negotiated and agreed to share the water equally again. Although the Queen would have still liked all of it, she had learnt that to take more than she needed had ended up hurting her most of all.

Alpha Behaviour

Being Alpha is about tending to be direct, defensive and dominant but you may be very sensitive if you feel you're being dominated.

Needing to be right, to win and to be respected is very important to you. It can mean that you feel extremely frustrated if you feel thwarted.

It can also lead to you having a command-and-control leadership style, where you may expect others to do things your way without particularly factoring in their perspective.

Although being Alpha has traditionally been related to being male, this is inaccurate because it's related less to gender and more to attitude.

In some businesses or families, this behaviour is taken for granted as normal.

Alpha Drivers

A tendency towards Alpha behaviour can be driven by many different things. These may include:

- **Anxiety** – feeling insecure and overcompensating by appearing bolder than you feel
- **Confidence** – mistakenly believing that dominance is the same as confidence
- **Control** – feeling uncomfortable if you're not in control, as well as taking more control than is your due
- **Hurt** – having been hurt in the past, tending to not trust others and being less generous with your opinions of others as a result
- **Inadequacy** – deep down feeling that others are more important than you, and trying to prove to everyone that you're just as good as they are
- **Modelling** – copying the Alpha behaviour of others because you mistakenly believe that's empowerment
- **Perfectionism** – having unreasonably high expectations of others in a range of areas

The good news is that being Alpha is a habit that can be changed with time and motivation, it's not a permanent character trait.

Positives of Alpha Behaviour

Having a tendency towards Alpha behaviour is likely to mean:

- Others may appreciate your boldness and ask you to be active on their behalf. You may, therefore, find yourself in the **role of spokesperson** or activist on behalf an individual or group

- You achieve **quick results**

- You may be able to make **tough decisions**, for example, during a war or in serious life or death circumstances

- You may be exceptionally **decisive in crisis situations**

- You may naturally be drawn to being **a leader**

Challenges of Alpha Behaviour

A tendency towards an Alpha approach can lead to three main challenges:

1. Being closed

2. A confrontational approach

3. Relationship challenges

 **Being Closed**

Here, you may:

- Be **unlikely to want to negotiate with others** and treat other perspectives - especially if they disagree with yours - as barriers to your agenda

- Be willing to **bluff and deny** your way through challenging situations

- **Defend yourself** when you receive constructive feedback, seeing it as criticism, rather than being open to it for personal growth

- Even if compromising or backing down is the most logical course of action, you won't want to do it due to keeping your **sense of pride**

- Have **black-and-white thinking** about what you believe is right and wrong rather than being open to ambiguity

- Insist that your views are right and try to **dominate agendas**

- **Keep information from others** to have the upper hand, wanting to be the most knowledgeable person in the room

- When faced with something you don't want to admit to, **lie** or try to pass it off as a joke or misunderstanding

 A Confrontational Approach

Here, you may:

- Be willing to **openly undermine or confront** someone who disagrees with you to try and get your own way

- Be willing to **use anger or aggression** - especially when you feel cornered and have run out of strategies

- **Intimidate others** so that they feel frightened of you. See this as leverage to influence them

- Potentially **spring confrontations** on others when they're not prepared, to wrong-foot them

- **Repeat back legitimate points** that someone else has said in a dismissive and challenging manner – as a tactic to undermine their point of view

- Use **attack as the best form of defence** to avoid admitting weakness

- Use **fake accusations** to distract others from issues you don't want to get into

 Relationship Challenges

Here, you may:

- Be **impatient** with others to put pressure on them to do things your way

- Be most comfortable **mixing with people who don't challenge you**

- Be willing to quickly **act put-out** in a disagreement to try and get sympathy, even if you don't really feel aggrieved

- **Create hostile atmospheres** by using micro-aggressions that leave others uneasy and vulnerable to your control

- Deliberately **ask for what you want when others are distracted** so that they agree to it without fully considering it

- **Feel frustrated** with people who don't agree with you

- **Grandstand** and behave in a showy manner to attract attention to your views especially if you feel that an alternative idea is getting attention

- Have a **low tolerance** for imperfection in others

- Have **little interest in the needs and feelings of others** when it comes to pursuing your goals

- **Prioritise getting your way** over supporting positive relationships

- **Tell others** what they should think and how they should feel and behave

- Use **persistence** to push your agenda to wear people down, so that they do what you want

- Use **unpredictability** as a tool of control - be pleasant when you feel others are supporting you. When they displease you, be hostile, so that they don't know where they stand with you

Consequences of Alpha Behaviour

Alpha behaviour can lead to the following consequences:

- Encouraging a stifling culture where **others don't feel free to express their opinions** as they retreat from your control

- Experiencing cumulative stress - leading you to become unwell which may worsen your behaviour, creating a **vicious cycle**

- **Feeling overwhelmed** as others may defer unnecessary decisions to you, as they don't feel empowered to act without your approval

- Finding line managers a source of frustration, as you're likely to **dislike being told what to do**

- Finding yourself **feeling misunderstood** and unpopular

- **Others may become alienated from you**, which may lead to them distancing themselves from you

- **Others may think of you as dishonest** leading to a lack of trust

- Others may try and get their own back on you, with negative gossip and/or **games played against you**, which fuels more mistrust

- You may be **accused of bullying** or find yourself in frequent conflict situations, which can seriously undermine your career and relationships

- You may be **labelled as 'difficult,'** leading to a poor reputation

- You may experience **sudden hostile outbursts from others** when people reach the limit of what they can stand and turn on you

- You may **fuel aggressive behaviour** in others by finding that your behaviour is mirrored back at you

- You may struggle to come to terms with the negative view others have about you and this may **affect your confidence**

- Your **support network may be limited** as you may find it challenging to keep a circle of supportive friends and colleagues in the long-term

 The biggest challenge of being Alpha is:

To stop quick-win controlling approaches and to replace them with collaboration, communication and compassion which leads to sustainable success.

☑ — **Suggested Strategies**
☑ —
☑ —

The strategies in this section are designed to support you to be empowered when you pursue what you need or to turn down an unwanted request.

One or two strategies may be very potent for you, or a combination of several may be effective. You'll need to experiment. However, some simply won't work for you; this is because we're all different.

It's likely that your Alpha behavioural habits will lessen over time, the more you focus on replacing them with empowered behaviours.

This Workbook can be used as a personal reflection tool and also for talking things through with a coach.

Consider analysing your behaviour in a journal/blog – note where you've done well and where you could improve.

It's possible that there may be sneaky reasons why you don't, at some level, want to address being Alpha.

Bearing this in mind, ask yourself: **'Do I feel comfortable changing my Alpha behaviours?'**

If, on reflection, you still feel unsure about addressing this, consider the Benefits of Empowerment (page 16) to remind yourself what amazing things you can achieve by working on this.

> **Reflection boxes in the next section are optional - do what suits you best. It may be that you need extra paper to write your thoughts. Alternatively, you may reflect through thinking, drawing, mind maps, music or art etc.**

Ambiguity: being comfortable navigating uncertainty

You may feel that you know what's best, after you've considered things in your own way. This may give you a feeling of certainty.

However, life is complex. **There are multiple ways of doing things and no one way is necessarily the 'right' way.**

You may have a tendency to want to resolve issues as soon as you can - to move things forward. You may also want to know as much as possible and be informed.

As much as you'd like this, knowing all the answers isn't possible. The good news is that others won't judge you for being unsure.

Consider embracing uncertainty. It may seem counter-intuitive but saying 'I don't know' is actually a strength. It leaves you open to creative possibilities, learning, and engagement with others.

 Affirmation

> **I embrace ambiguity.**

How to use Affirmations: Repeat these in your head or out loud 5 times every morning when you get up and 5 times when you go to bed. You can also repeat them at times of stress. It may seem silly at first (!) but these ideas will start to embed in your mind over time.

My Reflection

I could consider being more open to ambiguity because...

 Tips from the Coach

- Deliberately and curiously look at issues to see if there's another potential way to resolve them

- It can be freeing to not always be the one with the answers

2 Blame: assessing your contribution to challenging situations

Focusing on another person as your 'enemy,' can lead to you blaming them for negatively affecting your life. This narrative is likely to blight how you feel about them and deteriorates your relationship with them. It's also likely to lead to stress when you interact with them.

The truth is that others can only blight your life if you let them.

Believing that you've an enemy gives power to that person, due to the time you spend thinking about them. You may also feed negative emotions within yourself such as resentment and bitterness, which aren't helpful for you.

Attempt to reduce unrealistic expectations you may have of how others should behave. You don't have to forget what they have done, or are doing, but it can be freeing to simply let go of more minor annoyances.

Tell yourself: **'I've thought as much as I want to about this person. It's time to move on and focus on something more positive in my life.'**

In situations where you feel that others are undermining you, there are avenues available to get a solution. This might be to have a clear conversation or to seek help from someone else to mediate between you. Whatever route you take, try to deal with the matter at hand. Avoid going over the bad behaviour of the person involved in your mind as this may fuel Alpha behaviour in yourself.

Affirmation

> **I'm able to put resentment behind me and move on.**

How to use Affirmations: Repeat these in your head or out loud 5 times every morning when you get up and 5 times when you go to bed. You can also repeat them at times of stress. It may seem silly at first (!) but these ideas will start to embed in your mind over time.

 Tips from the Coach

- Ignore annoying behaviour you find in others
- If it's more serious, talk to the person who's affecting you about what's bothering you - with the aim of resolving the issue
- Thinking that you've an enemy wastes your time and energy
- Being more accepting of imperfections in others will cause you less stress

🌩 **My Reflection**

I could consider avoiding blame because...

3 Body language: focusing on being neutral when communicating

It's possible to present yourself in a more approachable and neutral way through your body language. Consider the following when you're communicating:

- Aim for a **relaxed expression** and limit tension in your face by smiling

- Avoid leaning into the personal space of the person you're communicating with, which is about a metre from them i.e., **don't get too close**

- **Look the other person in the eye** from time-to-time, avoiding an intense stare

- **Show that you're interested** in the other person's point of view when they're speaking by using an 'interested head tilt' and 'triple nodding'

- **Sit at the same eye level** as the person you're with and avoid standing above them or sitting in a chair that's higher than theirs

- Unfold your arms and uncross your legs – to **appear less defensive**

- Walk with a **calm, relaxed pace,** rather than fast striding – the energy you give off should be relaxed and positive

These are non-verbal clues which indicates that you feel equal to others. It also has the benefit of you appearing approachable.

Affirmation

> **I put people at their ease.**

How to use Affirmations: Repeat these in your head or out loud 5 times every morning when you get up and 5 times when you go to bed. You can also repeat them at times of stress. It may seem silly at first (!) but these ideas will start to embed in your mind over time.

 Tips from the Coach

- Aim for calmness and positivity in the way that you move and express yourself

- Keep a respectful distance and smile when you're communicating

☁ **My Reflection**

I could consider using more neutral body language because...

Boundaries: considering being more flexible with your rules

4

When you're approached by others with a request, you may be likely to say 'No' if it doesn't appear to benefit you. In other words, you may have a 'reflex No'.

You'll have created your boundaries to protect yourself from being pushed to do things that you don't want to do. This approach is good because it will enable you to achieve your goals. However, make sure that you've a balance between doing things for yourself and doing things for other people. **This is because too many fixed boundaries can potentially limit your opportunities and push people away.**

Supporting others and paying it forward can have the bonus of creating valuable good-will towards you. As we're socially inter-connected it's better to have a reputation for being helpful. Ideally, you should have a genuine desire to be helpful. If this isn't there, then you may need to be more supportive than is your natural inclination.

Opportunities such as new experiences can stretch you in interesting directions. You may learn something about yourself and develop by saying 'Yes' to requests made of you. You can never be sure where things might lead.

When a request is made of you, ask yourself: **'Could I consider saying 'Yes' rather than my usual 'reflex No' in this instance?'**

Affirmation

> I'm open to letting new
> experiences into my life.

How to use Affirmations: Repeat these in your head
or out loud 5 times every morning when you get up and
5 times when you go to bed. You can also repeat them
at times of stress. It may seem silly at first (!) but these
ideas will start to embed in your mind over time.

 Tips from the Coach

- When you feel that you're about to say 'No,' pause to
  consider whether this might be an opportunity you're
  letting go by

- Paying it forward can support your reputation and happiness

☁ My Reflection

I could consider when to flex my boundaries because...

Collaboration: relinquishing being the leader

Things would be simple and easy if you say what happens, people agree with you and then do as you say. Your needs will be met. What could be better than that?

The reality is that we live in an inter-dependent world and having control is a myth.

Having a tendency to be Alpha can mean that you may take power from others, through the force of your will. As power is taken, rather than given freely to you, it will be taken back – at the next available opportunity. An example of this might be in the form of, say, overturning your decisions when you move on to another job at work.

Rather than using control, consider using more collaboration. Collaboration with others means:

- Asking for opinions

- Being open to alternative viewpoints to find the best one

- Deciding a way forward by seeking a consensus

It's true that collaborative approaches will take longer to conclude an issue, rather than just deciding something yourself. However, in the long-term, the way forward is likely to be much more sustainable because it will have everyone's agreement.

Ask yourself: **'Do I sometimes get my own way when I know others don't agree with me?'**

If your answer is: **'Yes'** Ask yourself: **'How could I be more collaborative?'**

Affirmation

> **I work with others to seek consensus.**

How to use Affirmations: Repeat these in your head or out loud 5 times every morning when you get up and 5 times when you go to bed. You can also repeat them at times of stress. It may seem silly at first (!) but these ideas will start to embed in your mind over time.

 Tips from the Coach

- Taking power from others against their will only leads to short-term wins

- Sustainable approaches and decisions are ones where people agree on a way forward

☁ **My Reflection**

I could consider being more collaborative because...

6 Compassion: engaging your empathy

Although achievements are important, the relationships that underpin getting the job done mean more. You'll not have a total success unless you put energy both into what you're doing and compassionately considering the needs of those people who make it happen.

Look at your behaviour and consciously stop any 'rank and yank' directorial approaches you may have as a leader or manager. Instead, engage directly with others and motivate them by having a genuine interest in them and care for their wellbeing and needs.

Although others will have their flaws, most people try and do their best. They'll thrive on praise and wither on criticism. So, nurturing them by telling them what they're doing well is likely to bring out the best in them.

Fault-finding - to show someone how to improve – is likely to make them feel criticised. Think about balancing constructive feedback with what they're doing well. In fact, generally aim to increase the amount of praise you give to others.

> Ask yourself: **'What do I appreciate about this person (and their work), that I haven't shared with them?'** Once you've identified it, then tell them.

Also consider asking them how they are – not just with a cursory 'how are you?' but genuinely probing and listening to the answer. Aim to be empathetic and supportive where necessary.

It's also important to consider self-compassion and not to criticise yourself. If you notice that you're doing that, tell yourself: 'I'm doing the best I can, and perfection isn't possible.' And then follow this up with an activity which increases your wellbeing.

Affirmation

> **I'm interested in supporting other people's needs as well as my own.**

How to use Affirmations: Repeat these in your head or out loud 5 times every morning when you get up and 5 times when you go to bed. You can also repeat them at times of stress. It may seem silly at first (!) but these ideas will start to embed in your mind over time.

 Tips from the Coach

- To bring out the best in others, consider getting to know them better, praising them and supporting their needs

- Show loyalty to yourself by caring for your own needs and avoiding self-criticism

☁ My Reflection

I could consider being more compassionate towards myself and others because...

Conflict: moving from 'confrontations' to 'clear conversations'

When you're in a conflict your first instinct may be to confront, accuse and then defend. This approach is about basically doing all you can to prove that you're right and to get back control.

In the short-term, this can be an effective way to shut down a conflict. However, in the long-term, it's likely to damage relationships. Not only will those directly involved be affected but also their network will learn of it, which can be reputationally damaging.

The 'all guns blazing' confrontational approach also closes the possibility of flexibly and curiously considering alternative solutions to the issue.

Moving from: 'I want to win, and I want you to lose,' to 'how can we both resolve this and move on?' helps to reframe the situation from being a confrontation to being a clear conversation. A good mediation is one way to help create an agreed solution.

The process of seeing things from another perspective means that you'll learn, sometimes surprising information about the situation.

In challenging situations, step back and ask yourself:
'Do I need to confront someone with this, or can I consider talking to them about a solution with a clear conversation?'

Affirmation

> **I address issues without creating conflict.**

How to use Affirmations: Repeat these in your head or out loud 5 times every morning when you get up and 5 times when you go to bed. You can also repeat them at times of stress. It may seem silly at first (!) but these ideas will start to embed in your mind over time.

 Tips from the Coach

- Be open to learning more about the perspectives of the person or people you're in conflict with as you'll always learn something new

- Taking an 'I Win-you Lose' approach can have long-term negative repercussions

- Clear conversations are the empowered way to negotiate challenging situations

My Reflection

I could consider resolving conflict with a clear conversation because...

8 Consistency: becoming more predictable

When things go your way, you may feel kind towards others, as your mood is up-beat. However, if things aren't going your way, especially if people don't behave in the way that you want, you may start to show Alpha behaviours. Here, your thoughts and then emotions change to something more negative. This may appear to others as a lack of patience and too much directness.

You may not be aware of your changeability, but it will be obvious to those around you. For people who are more sensitive, this can put them on edge as they worry about what mood you're going to be in and how this will affect them.

It's key to watch your thoughts, emotions and behaviour if you feel that your mood is fluctuating and becoming negative. What you need is supportive people around you when things get stressful, rather than defensive people who stay out of your way.

No matter what you think and feel, remain respectful towards others. Rather than fluctuating emotionally, consider the strategies in the **Managing Emotions Workbook: Including Stress and Anger** in the **Coaching Psychology Series** to support you with reducing negative emotions and their impact.

Also consider consistency in terms of who is, or isn't, in your 'good books'. Instead of categorising people by having an 'in' and 'out' group, make every effort to behave fairly towards everyone, no matter how they behave.

The challenge here is that it's easier to be kinder to people you get on with and are like you. However, especially if you're a manager, it's your job to be impartial with your team – and you'll be respected for that.

Affirmation

> **I consistently treat everyone with respect and kindness.**

How to use Affirmations: Repeat these in your head or out loud 5 times every morning when you get up and 5 times when you go to bed. You can also repeat them at times of stress. It may seem silly at first (!) but these ideas will start to embed in your mind over time.

 Tips from the Coach

- Treat everyone respectfully and you won't go wrong
- Manage your emotions to keep your mood from dipping
- Don't put people into 'in' and 'out' categories and have favourites

☁ **My Reflection**

I could consider being more consistent towards others because...

Courtesy: the benefits of politeness and tact

Don't underestimate the power of courtesy to improve your relationships. **Be courteous to everyone, no matter who they are or what situation you're in.**

Being tactful and diplomatic is likely to bring out the best in others. It's also likely that you'll be treated with courtesy and respect in return. Consider the following ways to achieve this:

- Acknowledge another person's point of view so that they feel listened to, you could do this by **summarising** what they've said

- Always avoid getting personal, by saying things like: 'you always interfere'. Instead, **stick to the issue,** by saying 'Let's talk about where our responsibilities lie'

- **Be careful how you communicate** if you're feeling negative emotions

- **Draw on genuine positive feelings** that you want to do your best by other people when you communicate with them

- **Pay compliments** to others, for example, for good work, including publicly

- **Provide information** to others in good time when it's asked for, even if it's not a priority for you

- **Thank someone** for their kindness and support, for example, via a gift, card or message etc

- **Use politeness** to start and finish all emails no matter who they're to, such as: 'I hope you're well' and 'Best wishes' etc. Don't just sign off an email with your name or initial

- When writing, **consider introducing more of what you would say if you were communicating face-to-face** such as 'How are you?' 'How are the kids?' etc

Affirmation

> **I'm always polite and respectful.**

How to use Affirmations: Repeat these in your head or out loud 5 times every morning when you get up and 5 times when you go to bed. You can also repeat them at times of stress. It may seem silly at first (!) but these ideas will start to embed in your mind over time.

 Tips from the Coach

- Bring out the best in others by being polite
- Frequently show appreciation

☁ **My Reflection**

I could consider being more consistently courteous because...

Culture: navigating high Alpha environments

The environment that you're in will affect how you behave. Alpha behaviour may be approved of by, say, your workplace or family culture. You may feel that you must fit in by following suit.

Showing Alpha behaviour may come naturally to you, or you may experience subtle pressures to behave in that way. The latter is likely to cause you stress. Either way, being Alpha takes its toll because of constantly being in control.

You may want to consider role modelling empowered behaviour to attempt to change the culture you're in. You could also challenge other people when you see them showing Alpha behaviours.

If this isn't a task that appeals to you and you feel that the environment is toxic, you may want to consider leaving your situation and moving to a more sympathetic one where expectations are different.

Affirmation

> I challenge Alpha behaviour
> in myself and others.

How to use Affirmations: Repeat these in your head or out loud 5 times every morning when you get up and 5 times when you go to bed. You can also repeat them at times of stress. It may seem silly at first (!) but these ideas will start to embed in your mind over time.

 Tips from the Coach

- If you feel it's expected that you should show Alpha behaviour where you live or work, it would be wise to consider if this is a good fit for you

- There's nothing stopping you being a role model for empowerment in all situations

☁️ My Reflection

I could consider ways culture affects my behaviour because...

Denial: encouraging self-awareness

You may be in the habit of moving from one activity to another with minimal reflection. If this resonates with you, **it may be time to analyse your instinctive behaviours.**

Ask yourself:

'A lot of times am I the only person who I feel can get things done well?'

'Am I willing to be dominant when I feel cornered?'

'Do I feel more critical of people than warm about them?'

'Do I get easily frustrated with other people?'

'Do I hide information?

'Do I regularly feel that I can't trust people?'

'Do I tell lies to get my own way?'

Spend time honestly reflecting on the areas where you've said 'Yes'. Be particularly alert if you make excuses about why you do any of these things.

In these areas, think about the effect your approach is having on yourself and how it may be affecting others. You may be building up stress, anxiety and a lack of trust.

Ask yourself: **'What could I do differently?'**

You may benefit from working on this further with a coach or therapist to learn more about yourself.

Affirmation

> **I reflect on my behaviour in order to improve.**

How to use Affirmations: Repeat these in your head or out loud 5 times every morning when you get up and 5 times when you go to bed. You can also repeat them at times of stress. It may seem silly at first (!) but these ideas will start to embed in your mind over time.

 Tips from the Coach

- Take time to consider any less than flattering behaviours you may have

- Don't either be too hard on yourself or defend what's true about yourself as these are barriers to self-development

- Treat this deep-dive as a fascinating exploration which can potentially transform your behaviour and make you feel much less stressed

My Reflection

I could consider being more reflective because...

12 Diffusing situations: communicating with challenging people

As tempting as it is to react strongly to someone who's showing Alpha behaviour, this is likely to have the unhappy outcome of escalating a situation, rather than diffusing it. The only exception is if you're faced with the threat of a physical attack.

Looking at a more common and less extreme situation, for example, being openly criticised at work, an Alpha response would be to say: 'Don't speak to me like that again or I'll take out a grievance against you with HR!'

The empowered alternative would be:

'I hear your concerns about how we work together' **(acknowledging).** 'I believe that there are things that we can do to improve this' **(staying positive).** 'I'd like to discuss this with you, but I think it would be more productive to pause until we have had a chance to properly think things through and not involve other people at this stage,' **(taking control and reducing emotion).** 'I suggest we meet later to talk about this to work out a way forward together,' **(being constructive).**

Then, when you meet to discuss the issue, question, listen and draw out the other person's perspective using phrases such as: **'Talk me through what happened from your perspective.'** You can also explain your own thoughts and feelings to create mutual understanding.

It takes time, energy, control and thought to be empowered. However, the effort you put in, is well worth it for the sake of maintaining relationships for the future.

Affirmation

> I'm comfortable diffusing challenging situations.

How to use Affirmations: Repeat these in your head or out loud 5 times every morning when you get up and 5 times when you go to bed. You can also repeat them at times of stress. It may seem silly at first (!) but these ideas will start to embed in your mind over time.

 Tips from the Coach

- Meet aggression with calmness
- When you're having a clear conversation listen, reflect, speak and use solution-focused approaches to enable a resolution
- Expect that it will take time and energy to diffuse a challenging situation using empowered techniques

☁ **My Reflection**

I could consider managing challenging people better because...

13 Feedback: analysing how you're viewed by others

Consider asking for feedback about your behaviour from trusted friends and colleagues. It's worth being specific about what you would like them to comment on. Specifically ask if you ever come over as dominant, aggressive or direct etc. Ask for specific examples to consider.

Attempt to get feedback from a range of people. You may want to consider 360° feedback processes, where managers, peers and team members give anonymous feedback.

Label the information you receive as feedback – rather than criticism. Encourage your curiosity. Feedback potentially holds information about your blind spots, which others can see.

Be particularly mindful not to become defensive if you receive uncomfortable information.

If what you hear or read appears irrelevant, take time to objectively analyse if there's a kernel of truth in the feedback, which could help you to develop. You may want to consider working with a coach to better understand the feedback and what it means to you.

Once you've identified your learning points, consider what you may want to change about your behaviour to become more empowered.

Affirmation

> **Getting feedback is a fantastic way to develop myself.**

How to use Affirmations: Repeat these in your head or out loud 5 times every morning when you get up and 5 times when you go to bed. You can also repeat them at times of stress. It may seem silly at first (!) but these ideas will start to embed in your mind over time.

 Tips from the Coach

- Ask for feedback about your behaviour, particularly with regard to being direct and Alpha
- Be curious about the feedback, even if it's challenging
- Decide your learning and action points to develop yourself

My Reflection

I could consider being positive about receiving feedback because...

Friendliness: considering the importance of social bonds

Prioritising putting time into relationships to build trust and increase your social network is time well spent.

Networks enable the voluntary giving and receiving of information and support. This is the main alternative to Alpha behaviour which tries to get to the same outcome through control.

This isn't about making people like you. It's about attempting to build genuine friendships and rapport. Getting to know people – what they like, where they live, who their families are and what's important to them will help to create connections between you. Being friendly and showing an interest is all-important. Ideally your intent should be to want to create genuine social bonds or, failing that, to be kind, interested and respectful to people.

If you tend to be distant, attempt to build rapport. Your conversations should be less about yourself and more about the person you're talking to. But be willing to be open about yourself too. This will mean that they're building a social bond with you too as they get to know you more.

Not only does friendliness lead to supportive relationships but it also will make your life happier and more meaningful.

Affirmation

> **I prioritise my relationships.**

How to use Affirmations: Repeat these in your head or out loud 5 times every morning when you get up and 5 times when you go to bed. You can also repeat them at times of stress. It may seem silly at first (!) but these ideas will start to embed in your mind over time.

 Tips from the Coach

- Strong relationships in your network will provide support at times when you need them

- The closer you get to others, the more redundant your Alpha behaviours will become

💭 My Reflection

I could consider being more friendly to others because...

Hearing 'No': how to respond when someone turns you down

It can be challenging to be turned down – whether this is about something minor, or something important. You may feel disappointed, frustrated and hurt.

Your first instinct may be to try and change the person's mind. As a rule of thumb, don't, if it's not essential. If you do try, be mindful that you may be pushing another person's boundaries by challenging their decision.

When a colleague resigns for example – be dignified and let them go! People have free will to move on if they need to. Don't dismiss their choice out of pride or take it personally. Instead tell yourself: **'Just as I need to say 'No' sometimes – so do other people'** and then move on.

Ultimately, don't try and hang on to relationships that are over. As hard as it can be, respect other people's choices by letting them go.

 Affirmation

> ## I respect other people's free will.

How to use Affirmations: Repeat these in your head or out loud 5 times every morning when you get up and 5 times when you go to bed. You can also repeat them at times of stress. It may seem silly at first (!) but these ideas will start to embed in your mind over time.

My Reflection

I could consider being more accepting of hearing 'No' because...

 Tips from the Coach

- Don't take rejection personally, it's just the result of someone exercising their free will

- At times it's right to let people go

16 Intentional passivity: deliberately stepping back to let situations develop

You may be in the habit of being dynamic and decisive.

There's another approach that you may under-use though. This is to deliberately **not** act. It may seem counter-intuitive that sitting back and waiting means that you're being empowered. But what you're actively doing is creating space for the situation to evolve.

It's potentially a way of encouraging others to step up.
It also gives you a breather from responsibility.

To be clear, avoiding something that you don't want to do so that it slides is a completely different thing! This isn't what's meant by intentional passivity. Although both are essentially doing nothing, the difference is that intentional passivity means that you're still engaged by watching the situation. Avoidance is ignoring the situation altogether.

Affirmation

> Sometimes, I step back and let situations breathe.

How to use Affirmations: Repeat these in your head or out loud 5 times every morning when you get up and 5 times when you go to bed. You can also repeat them at times of stress. It may seem silly at first (!) but these ideas will start to embed in your mind over time.

 Tips from the Coach

- Intentionally being passive is a useful approach to let situations develop

- Stepping back means that you encourage others to take responsibility

- It can be a relief to not always be in control

My Reflection

I could consider choosing not to act sometimes because...

17 Listening: understanding others better

Spending time listening to the perspectives of others is useful, particularly in challenging relationships. You do this by drawing people out with questions to encourage them to talk. If there's a limited response to your questioning, then there's an issue with trust from the person you're talking to. To build trust, you may need to work on the relationship more over time. Alternatively, you may want to disclose something of yourself to model openness with them.

This approach isn't the soft, ineffective choice because listening to the point of view of others gives useful information.

You may have the belief that you have to build up to a discussion, but this isn't true. You can swiftly get to the point if you want to. You could start a conversation by saying: **'Let's talk about how things went yesterday. What are your thoughts?'** Your intention is to provide a safe opportunity to explore their point of view.

Ask coaching questions that encourage people to open up like: **'What's the real issue here for you?'**

Rather than jumping in with a solution, step back. It's better for them to decide solutions for themselves. Avoid interrupting, let them have their say.

If you feel that they need to know something important, say: **'I've an observation, I'd like to share with you'** and then explain yourself in a concise, neutral way.

At the end of the conversation ask: **'So what are next steps do you think?'**

Do what you say you're going to do. If you say: **'I'd really like to hear your views on this,'** then carefully listen.

Consider summarising what you've heard to check your understanding and then say: **'Is there something that I've missed or misunderstood?'**

Consider **attuned listening** where you focus more on the person you're talking to, than yourself. If you're ever in doubt about whether you practice attuned listening, ask the person you're communicating with: **'Do you feel that I've really listened to you today?'**

Coaching style communication isn't quick. In fact, consider setting aside four or five times more time to resolve an issue than you're likely to be used to if you've a more Alpha style. What you're investing in is the future relationship. **The other benefits of this approach can be:**

- Connecting at a deeper – perhaps emotional - level
- Getting someone to commit to their own solutions
- Having a full understanding of another perspective
- Learning new information

 **Affirmation**

> **I'm a good listener.**

How to use Affirmations: Repeat these in your head or out loud 5 times every morning when you get up and 5 times when you go to bed. You can also repeat them at times of stress. It may seem silly at first (!) but these ideas will start to embed in your mind over time.

My Reflection

I could consider listening more because...

 ## Tips from the Coach

- Listening isn't the soft choice – it requires empathy and concentration

- Take time to get to know people and their motivations with a coaching approach to conversations

- Short-term directive communication styles don't create long-term sustainable relationships

18 Needs and wants: deciding goals which give your life meaning

What you **need** is what gives your life fulfilment and happiness. What you **want** relates to what you would prefer to happen and items that you would like to own. Wants are things that, if you thought about it, you could compromise about.

It's time well spent to reflect on your needs and wants.

Examples of your needs might be:
- Achieving positive change in your career
- Actively engaging with charitable work
- Caring for your family
- Driving your career
- Feeling autonomous
- Having intellectual challenge
- Having secure finances
- Having time to pursue your creativity and hobbies
- Practising your chosen spirituality or religion
- Prioritising your mental and physical health
- Spending time with close friends

After reflecting, if you're not sure about your needs and wants you may benefit from seeking support from a coach to help clarify this with you. Your goals are based on your needs. Your needs will change over time and so they'll need to be periodically reviewed.

Crucially, when thinking about where to spend your energy and time, this should be on your needs, not your wants.

Affirmation

> I know what to prioritise and what to relax about.

How to use Affirmations: Repeat these in your head or out loud 5 times every morning when you get up and 5 times when you go to bed. You can also repeat them at times of stress. It may seem silly at first (!) but these ideas will start to embed in your mind over time.

 Tips from the Coach

- Knowing your needs gives you a clear rationale of where to focus
- You can relax about your wants

My Reflection

I could consider being clearer about my needs and wants because...

Positivity: addressing negative thinking

19

Being empowered is based on an attitude that most people are trustworthy and do the best they can. This attitude will encourage you to appreciate their strengths and be more forgiving of their mistakes.

This isn't the same as **toxic positivity** which ignores anything negative. But you also don't want to be overly negative either, which is also a bias and can fuel Alpha behaviour.

When your thoughts stray to being negative, aim to seek rational balance by deliberately thinking about what's good to balance up.

By looking at what's good, you're likely to:

- Be more trusting of others
- Feel more optimistic
- Focus less on blame
- Relinquish some control
- See more opportunities

Positive thoughts are closely linked to positive emotions. Managing emotions is a complex area and if you feel that you would benefit from support with this, try the **Managing Emotions Workbook: Including Stress and Anger** in the **Coaching Psychology Series.**

Affirmation

> **I believe in the good in others.**

How to use Affirmations: Repeat these in your head or out loud 5 times every morning when you get up and 5 times when you go to bed. You can also repeat them at times of stress. It may seem silly at first (!) but these ideas will start to embed in your mind over time.

 Tips from the Coach

- Negative thoughts and emotions can create Alpha behaviours

- Seeking balanced thoughts which factor in a positive perspective creates a good foundation for empowered behaviour

My Reflection

I could consider being more positive because…

20 Reflection: analysis before action

Empowered behaviour is based on taking time to consider how you're going to act before you do so. Reflect on the **smart move**, which is in your best interests, rather than following your first instinctive **reflex reaction**.

The reason for this is because that reflex reaction may be coming from a protective place from within you which may mistakenly see your situation as a threat. This means that your reflex reaction is likely to be an over-reaction.

When deciding the smart move, you may want to imagine the perspectives of others to different hypothetical scenarios based on the action you're considering taking. If this type of thinking is challenging for you, then you may want to consider talking about other people's perspectives with a colleague or coach.

The following prompts may help with your reflection. Ask yourself:

'How can I influence rather than direct in this situation?'

'What's my ideal outcome?'

'How are others likely to react if I take this course of action?'

'How can I meet the needs of others?'

'Is it possible that I might be missing information? If so, how do I go about finding it?'

'What options do I have to approach this situation?'

'Who's not on board with my view?'

Whatever your situation, this approach may seem like a lot of work when compared with your gut instinct! However, it's worth the effort because the results are likely to be successful and sustainable, due to the important reflective time you've put in.

✓ **Affirmation**

> **I'm a strategist.**

How to use Affirmations: Repeat these in your head or out loud 5 times every morning when you get up and 5 times when you go to bed. You can also repeat them at times of stress. It may seem silly at first (!) but these ideas will start to embed in your mind over time.

 Tips from the Coach

- Investing time in working out the best course of action will pay dividends in the future
- Be wary of automatically acting on your instincts

My Reflection

I could consider reflecting more because...

21 Saying 'No': respectfully turning someone down

It may be straightforward for you to turn someone down if they ask you to do something that you don't want to do.

Having boundaries to protect your needs is useful for preserving your time and energy. However, think about the way that you do it and whether you might be saying 'No' too much.

When you turn people down the idea is to leave the relationship intact by being respectful. The last thing you want is to make people feel offended by your lack of support. Instead of perhaps being direct, consider starting your response with gratitude. An example is: **'I'm grateful that you've thought of me, but I can't'.**

Although this is frowned on by traditional assertive theories, you may wish to give a reason for turning someone down, depending on the situation and person involved. There's no need to use false excuses to try and soften the blow though. Just be polite and clear, for example, by saying: **'I can't help you because I'm working on a project which is taking up a lot of my free time'.**

You may also want to consider acknowledging their disappointment by saying: **'I appreciate this is probably not the response you'd hoped for, but I hope this gets resolved for you soon'.**

Consider if there are other people who could support instead and if you feel it's appropriate suggest alternatives, to show good-will.

Affirmation

> I'm respectful of other people's needs.

How to use Affirmations: Repeat these in your head or out loud 5 times every morning when you get up and 5 times when you go to bed. You can also repeat them at times of stress. It may seem silly at first (!) but these ideas will start to embed in your mind over time.

 Tips from the Coach

- By respectfully saying 'No' you show empathy to the requester

- Explaining why you can't do something is an option you may want to take to be understood

💭 My Reflection

I could consider how I turn people down because...

22 Speech: how to use your voice

Consider the tone of your voice so that it reflects empowered behaviour, especially if you can:

- Be careless with your choice of language

- Talk quickly

- Talk loudly

- Talk too much

Empowered speech is natural and friendly. Below are tips to achieve this:

- Avoid controlling words like: 'you should...'

- Avoid dismissive phrases like: 'I understand but...'

- Avoid getting personal by, for example, saying: 'you always...'

- Avoid patronising words like: 'well, obviously...'

- Avoid provocative phrases like: 'You're being aggressive...'

- Avoid repetitively asking: 'Why?'

- Cut down what you say if you talk a lot, especially if you tend to talk over others

- Reduce the volume of your speech if you're loud. Don't shout unless there's a really good reason (such as shouting out to tell someone not to cross the road in front of a car!)

- Slow down the speed of your speech if you talk too quickly. It will have the bonus of helping you to feel and appear calmer

Affirmation

> **I'm a sensitive communicator.**

How to use Affirmations: Repeat these in your head or out loud 5 times every morning when you get up and 5 times when you go to bed. You can also repeat them at times of stress. It may seem silly at first (!) but these ideas will start to embed in your mind over time.

 Tips from the Coach

- How you speak is as important as what you're saying
- The tone you use shows your intent and emotions to the person you're communicating with

☁ **My Reflection**

I could consider how I use my voice because…

23 Stepping back: using time-outs for yourself

You may experience frustration which leads to you showing Alpha behaviour. An example of this might be seeing indecisiveness in others which triggers you to become impatient.

If you believe that anger is contributing to your Alpha behaviour, consider the **Managing Emotions Workbook: Including Stress and Anger.** This Workbook has many strategies to support getting emotional control.

One strategy to avoid showing your frustration to others, is to remove yourself from a situation when you feel provoked. Simply say: 'Excuse me' leave and head for the toilet where you can (usually!) be guaranteed quiet, private space.

Use the quiet time away from the provoking situation productively. Say to yourself: **'I'm now in a time-out where I'll logically focus on how to manage my emotions and decide a way forward'.**

Whatever your circumstances, only return when you're back in control and have a plan. If you don't feel that it's essential that you contribute and you still feel frustrated, then make your excuses and leave. It's better to keep control and exit calmly, than to 'lose it' publicly.

Step back from potential triggers before going to bed. An example might be avoiding reading work emails before you sleep. In other words, prioritise and protect your rest because rest is essential to have the headspace to manage stressors.

If you can't get away from a situation and still feel triggered, you could consider stepping back verbally by saying: **'I need time to think about this. I'll respond later'.**

Affirmation

> # When I feel frustrated, I can step back.

How to use Affirmations: Repeat these in your head or out loud 5 times every morning when you get up and 5 times when you go to bed. You can also repeat them at times of stress. It may seem silly at first (!) but these ideas will start to embed in your mind over time.

 ## Tips from the Coach

- Anger feeds Alpha behaviour. If you feel that anger is an issue for you, take time to address this

- It's better to leave a situation that's triggering you, than to show frustration to others

- Prioritise sleep to have the ability to be more relaxed around potential stressors

💭 My Reflection

I could consider stepping back because…

24 Therapy: considering the roots of your behaviour

It can be useful to explore why you behave as you do with a professional counsellor or therapist. This is particularly important if you find managing your emotions is challenging or if you've experienced trauma. Having insight into yourself, means that you'll find it easier to develop empowered behaviours because you'll build on a strong knowledgebase.

You may have copied Alpha behaviour patterns from role models in your past, such as parents/caregivers, which may not be helpful to you. You may also be automatically reacting to situations based on protective emotional patterns you've developed from your past.

Your workplace may offer access to confidential counselling services which can be a useful resource. GPs may also have counselling services you can access. Private counsellors are also available face-to-face, online and on the phone. Some professional memberships also offer counselling.

> You could also consider hypnotherapy, which works through deep relaxation to positively influence you at a sub-conscious level. This is particularly useful to remove unhelpful subconscious behaviour patterns.

In all cases, work with a therapist who has been professionally trained and is registered with an approved body.

Affirmation

> **I'm open to exploring my inner self with a therapist.**

How to use Affirmations: Repeat these in your head or out loud 5 times every morning when you get up and 5 times when you go to bed. You can also repeat them at times of stress. It may seem silly at first (!) but these ideas will start to embed in your mind over time.

 Tips from the Coach

- Therapy can give you clarity about why you behave in the way that you do

- Hypnotherapy can work at a sub-conscious level to free you from unhelpful automatic behaviour patterns

My Reflection

I could consider therapy because...

25 Vulnerability: being authentic with others

A hospice nurse found that one of the top five regrets of dying people was not expressing their feelings at key moments in their life.[1]

Sometimes a tendency to have Alpha behaviour means masking your thoughts and feelings. You may believe that opening up is uncomfortable and unnecessary. It may also seem like a loss of power, or you may be fearful of another person's reaction to really seeing you. But if you don't open up this can mean that you're locked in to being misunderstood.

Being vulnerable can create a close connection and understanding between you and the person you're communicating with. This means that you can be completely honest about your thoughts, feelings and behaviour, as vulnerable as this might make you feel. By doing so, you also model openness, which is likely to encourage others to open up about their needs and feelings too.

A **vulnerability hangover** is where you reflect on what you've said and later feel embarrassed. Treat this uncomfortable feeling as evidence of you being authentically and powerfully yourself.

Judge the effectiveness of being vulnerable by how the situation develops, **not** by the discomfort you may feel.

---

[1] Ware, B. (2012) *The Top Five Regrets of the Dying* Hay House

Affirmation

> I clearly explain what I need and feel.

How to use Affirmations: Repeat these in your head or out loud 5 times every morning when you get up and 5 times when you go to bed. You can also repeat them at times of stress. It may seem silly at first (!) but these ideas will start to embed in your mind over time.

 Tips from the Coach

- Pride can prevent you from being open about your needs and feelings. This can create a barrier to making connections with others

- Avoid later regret by being vulnerable when it's important to do so

☁ My Reflection

I could consider opening myself up to others more
because...

Goal setting

Take time to note your thoughts and plans relating to becoming empowered.

Ask yourself: **'How will I reward myself for working on this?'**

1

2

3

4

5

Passivity

Passivity Metaphor

> **The purpose of this metaphor is to tell a story about being passive. This story aims to communicate with your subconscious, rather than conscious mind. Your conscious mind will be engaging with the facts and information about empowerment while your subconscious mind prefers metaphors.**
>
> **If you're working with a hypnotherapist, this story could be incorporated into a trance session to help support your subconscious mind with being empowered.**

It was noisy in the jungle. At night, the animals would increase the sound of their cries and chatter. In fact, it was difficult to sleep - if you weren't used to it.

When this particular monkey had been younger, he had tried to cry out and chatter and hoot. But the other monkeys had laughed, teased and criticised these attempts. The monkey had decided to give up and say nothing. And he was known as 'mute monkey'.

In the tribe, mute monkey was expected to do many things for everyone else and, frankly, was taken for granted. It wasn't deliberate, but as mute monkey had no opinions, decisions were made for mute monkey by the tribe.

It was at night that the monkey felt most voiceless, not being able to contribute to the sounds that the others made. And when mute monkey thought about it, it was frustrating to be so quiet. Reflecting that years were passing by, was giving him pause for thought. Mute monkey wanted to make some changes.

One of the monkeys heard mute monkey grunting one day. And someone else heard mute monkey muttering. And, one night, mute monkey drew in a deep breath and began to hoot.

And strange and scary as it was, it also felt incredible.

The other monkeys reacted in different ways. Some were shocked, others joined in and supported mute monkey, and others simply just went on sleeping.

And mute monkey made bigger changes over time. Because the tribe couldn't take mute monkey for granted again, they learnt to get to know and respect the new voice and personality - which was lively, confident, and fun. They saw mute monkey in a completely different light.

The tribe gathered to decide what to call mute monkey now because that name didn't seem right anymore. And the tribe unanimously decided that mute monkey had a new name.

And mute monkey was known as 'cheeky monkey' from that day on.

Passivity

Passive behaviour means that you're likely to find it challenging to express your needs. You may prioritise other's needs and follow their lead. Rather than taking action you may let circumstances develop, without resistance. Setting boundaries with others may also be something that you would rarely consider doing.

Drivers for Passivity

Your passivity may be driven by a variety of factors, including:

- **Anxiety** – related to taking action and fearing making a mistake

- **Confidence** – not believing that you've the ability to be effective

- **Confusion** – not knowing your goals and so you do nothing

- **Laziness** – feeling that it just takes too much effort to be driven

- **People pleasing** – giving in to what others want of you, even if it's not what you want for yourself, to obtain their approval

- **Selfishness** – believing that others should come first and you're not a nice person if you prioritise your needs

Positives of Passivity

The positives of tending to be passive are that you may:

- Be considered easy to get on with and undemanding
- Prioritise nurturing others and be a caring person
- When you're led, you're likely to be a good follower

Challenges of Passivity

Unfortunately, there's a vicious cycle associated with a tendency to have passive behaviour. This is:

1

Allowing others to use your time and energy

which leads to

2

Sacrificing pursuing your needs

which leads to

3

Increased expectations from others about what you're willing to give

which leads to

4

Allowing others to use your time and energy...

and so on

A passive approach can also lead to two main challenges. They are:

1 Avoidant behaviour

2 Being a pushover

Avoidant behaviour

Here you:

- **Avoid making decisions** – big or small
- **Deal with things in writing** which would better be addressed face-to-face
- Disagree inwardly, but **agree** outwardly
- **Don't express your opinions** and retreat from engaging directly
- **Hope that someone will get the message** about your needs without telling them what the message is
- **Keep quiet** about reasonable doubts
- Tend to **avoid answering questions** from others if you feel challenged
- **Withdraw** when situations feel difficult

 Being a pushover

Here you:

- **Agree to requests** that you don't want to do
- Be **hustled into doing things** by others without giving yourself enough time to consider what you're agreeing to
- **Become overloaded** with work
- Communicate with an unconvincing **submissive tone**
- Find it extremely **challenging to express yourself** to more dominant people
- Tend **not to set reasonable boundaries**

 The biggest challenge of passivity is:

To be more honest and clear with yourself and others about your needs - and to act on these with enthusiasm.

Consequences of Passivity

There are two main consequences of passivity:

1 Issues with personal fulfilment

2 Emotional repression

 Issues with personal fulfilment

Here you:

- Are indirect, so **your needs may not easily be understood** or supported by others

- Are perceived by others as **not having potential** beyond your current role as your skills are well hidden

- **Don't have clear goals** and so find it challenging to know what direction to take for yourself

- **Go along with the choices other people make** for you in terms of your career and personal life

- **Lose personal power** by focusing on supporting other people with their goals, putting your needs at a low priority

- **Risk burnout** due to the expectations that are placed on you

 Emotional repression

Here you:

- Avoid expressing what you think or feel, due to a **fear of conflict**

- **Blame others** for the situation that you're in

- **Eventually feel bitter** due to your lack of fulfilment

- **Fear failure,** making you reluctant to give things a go

- Feel disappointed with your situation but **find it challenging to change** it

- Feel helpless and **depressed**

- **Feel resigned** to things being the way they are

- **Find yourself misunderstood** as your needs and feelings aren't clear to others

- Have **inner tension** between the way you present yourself and your thoughts and feelings

- **Lack enthusiasm** and come over to others as disengaged

- **Lack motivation** and feel stuck

- **Prefer others to take charge** but become passive-aggressive or resentful as a result

- Pretend that everything's OK and **hide your true feelings**

- **Privately feel hurt** for sometimes not being treated with respect

- Suddenly become angry due to **repressing frustration** – even if it's out of proportion to the situation that you're in

In extreme cases, smothering your emotions and needs can lead to something called **de-selfing**. De-selfing is a deep depression, combined with an emotional breakdown and a feeling of being lost, worthless and inauthentic. Here, you become psychologically disconnected from your identity. If things have reached this point, you urgently need to prioritise finding ways to nurture and express yourself by seeking the support of a therapist and advice from your GP.

☑— Suggested Strategies

The strategies in this section are designed to support you to be empowered when you pursue what you need or to turn down an unwanted request

One or two strategies may be very potent for you, or a combination of several may be effective. You'll need to experiment. However, some simply won't work for you; this is because we're all different.

It's likely that your passive behavioural habits will lessen over time, the more you focus on replacing them with empowered behaviours.

This Workbook can be used as a personal reflection tool and also for talking things through with a coach.

Consider analysing your behaviour in a journal/blog – note where you've done well and where you could improve.

It's possible that there may be sneaky reasons why you don't, at some level, want to address being passive.

Bearing this in mind, ask yourself: **'Do I feel comfortable changing my passive behaviours?'**

If, on reflection, you still feel unsure about addressing this, consider the Benefits of Empowerment (page 16) to remind yourself what amazing things you can achieve by working on this.

> **Reflection boxes in the next section are optional - do what suits you best. It may be that you need extra paper to write your thoughts. Alternatively, you may reflect through thinking, drawing, mind maps, music or art etc.**

Action: pursuing your goals with a Plan

You may feel that you're in an actionless zone. At first, this might have felt comfortable and safe. However, it might now feel a bit stifling, with too much on hold.

If you think about your life in terms of driving a bus, ask yourself:

'Am I in the driver's seat?'

'If I'm not in the driver's seat of my bus, where am I sitting?

Near the front, middle or at the back?

And who's driving my bus?'

'What would it take for me to move up the bus and become the driver?'

> Taking action to be more in control, can lead you in new, exciting and unpredictable directions. This may seem a little risky at first but the enriching experiences that come with it, will outweigh those risks.

Be wary of making excuses for inaction. If you're waiting for a time in the future to be ready to act, this could be a sign of procrastination.

Attitudes that are barriers to taking action are things like telling yourself:

- **'If I had enough money I would…'**
- **'If I was younger I would…'**
- **'If I had more time I would…'**
- **'If I had better health I would…'**

Like everyone, you can do amazing things without money, youth, time and perfect health. Ask yourself:

'What discomfort am I avoiding by doing nothing?'

Once you start creating a Plan to achieve your goals, the following can help shape and maintain that Plan:

- **Be realistic** about what can be achieved within a certain timeframe
- **Get information** if you don't have all the facts
- **Break down your goals** into smaller steps
- Take **one step at a time**
- **Keep reviewing** what's required
- You may want to **start with quick wins** to gather momentum
- **Consider contingency planning.** Tell yourself: 'If Plan A doesn't work, this is my Plan B' and give yourself an alternative – this will also help manage any anxiety

If you don't succeed with your Plan, this isn't a character flaw. It may just be an indication that you need to make a different one.

⊘ Affirmation

> **I'm in the driving seat of my life.**

How to use Affirmations: Repeat these in your head or out loud 5 times every morning when you get up and 5 times when you go to bed. You can also repeat them at times of stress. It may seem silly at first (!) but these ideas will start to embed in your mind over time.

Tips from the Coach

- When you take action, start off with small steps and easy wins to give you momentum

- Consider having a Plan B

- As you pursue your goals, be mindful of what you're achieving and how far you've come

☁ My Reflection

I could consider taking more action because...

Asking: getting what you need by requesting it

You may think it could be helpful to get advice, for example, about a career decision. However, you may also find that asking for help feels uncomfortable.

Rather than it being an imposition, many people find it flattering to be asked for help and are likely to do what they can to support you.

Ask yourself: '**What have I got to lose by asking for help?**'

> If you get turned down by one person, there will always be someone else who you can ask to support you. Think of yourself as part of a large network which you can draw on in creative ways.

This network is everyone you know, new or old colleagues, friends, family and everyone they know. All these people are potentially available to you and social media makes connecting with them easily accessible.

Once you've decided what you want and who you want it from, ask yourself: 'What's the best way for me to approach them?'

Consider where, when and how you'll ask. Then go for it. Make that call. Book that appointment. Send that email. Post that request online. Send out that teaser material in the post.

Be ready to ask specifically about what you need. If you're having a face-to-face meeting, avoid too much verbal filler such as: 'I wouldn't normally mention this, only I was just walking by your door and I wondered...' Instead, be clear and polite. An example is: **'Can I discuss some ideas I've got about my career development with you please?'**

Consider expressing your feelings if, for example, you feel overwhelmed. This puts the person you're talking to in the picture. You could say: 'I feel nervous asking you about this but...'

Be willing to concentrate and listen, to fully understand the other person's perspective.

Be open to supporting others when they ask for your support.

Affirmation

> **If I need something, I'll ask for it.**

How to use Affirmations: Repeat these in your head or out loud 5 times every morning when you get up and 5 times when you go to bed. You can also repeat them at times of stress. It may seem silly at first (!) but these ideas will start to embed in your mind over time.

My Reflection

I could consider asking for what I need because...

Tips from the Coach

- You're part of a network – consider drawing on it for support

- Think about how you'll approach people to find what you need

- Remember that most people like to be helpful

3 Being indirect: the pitfalls of hiding what you think and feel

You may be in the habit of being indirect about your needs. You may fear that being direct will lead to conversations that you'd prefer to avoid. You may also be glad that you can pretend that you didn't mean what you were hinting at if things get challenging later.

Rather than a clear conversation, you might give hints such as saying to your line manager: 'It seems like a lot of people are getting promoted around here...' rather than: **'I'd like to book time with you to discuss my career progression please.'**

There are several ways people can respond to indirectness, such as

1. They understand you but decide to do nothing – this shows some reluctance to support you

2. They understand that you're asking for something but misunderstand your needs - this can lead to confusion and potentially inappropriate actions being taken

3. They misunderstand that you're approaching them to get your needs met - which means that your approach is impotent

4. They try and engage you with a clear conversation about your needs – here you'll be encouraged to directly talk - whether you're ready to, or not!

All these outcomes ultimately mean that you hand over control of the discussion to someone else.

You won't know whether you're going to be satisfied or disappointed, unless you clearly ask for what you need. **By being more empowered, you'll not have later regrets about avoiding getting less than you deserve.**

Affirmation

> I politely tell it how it is.

How to use Affirmations: Repeat these in your head or out loud 5 times every morning when you get up and 5 times when you go to bed. You can also repeat them at times of stress. It may seem silly at first (!) but these ideas will start to embed in your mind over time.

 Tips from the Coach

- Being indirect with others can lead to confusion
- You hand over control to another person if you're indirect
- Being clear about what you need will enable you to get support for your goals

My Reflection

I could consider being clearer about my needs to others because...

Body language: appearing more empowered

Your body language indicates to others how confident you are. They'll therefore have an expectation about how assertive you're likely to be with them by the way you look and carry yourself.

Consider the ideas below when you want to appear more confident and empowered. The aim isn't to be fake but to bring out the most confident version of yourself.

- **Avoid uncomfortable clothes** – especially shoes - so that you can relax

- **Be attentive to the present moment** and the person you're with

- **Nod from time-to-time** when you're listening, to show that you're absorbing what they're saying

- **Sit or stand up straight** - avoid slumping

- **Tilt your head slightly to one side** when you look at someone as they're talking, to indicate that you're listening

- **Uncross your arms if they're folded**, to appear more approachable

- **Use a 'triple nod'** to encourage people to talk more

- **Use eye contact from time-to-time**, especially if you tend to look down or away from people when you're speaking

These techniques may feel unnatural at first but, like everything will seem less so over time, the more that you practice them.

If you're neurodiverse or have a physical disability, some of these suggestions may be challenging for you. If this is the case, be open about explaining how you uniquely express your thoughts and feelings to others.

 Affirmation

> **I have charisma.**

How to use Affirmations: Repeat these in your head or out loud 5 times every morning when you get up and 5 times when you go to bed. You can also repeat them at times of stress. It may seem silly at first (!) but these ideas will start to embed in your mind over time.

 Tips from the Coach

- Drawing out the most confident and empowered version of yourself will help you appear less passive

- Whatever your circumstances, use your individuality to supercharge appearing empowered

💭 **My Reflection**

I could consider empowered body language because...

Boundaries: deciding what you will and won't accept from others

Setting boundaries is about protecting yourself from situations where your energy leaks away in directions that suit other people. Boundaries are especially important if you've a **'reflex Yes'** to requests made of you. Setting boundaries is a key way to prevent stress.

> Boundaries aren't just for work and can be applied to all areas of your life, such as with family, friends, pets and romantic relationships.

To get clarity about what boundaries to set, consider completing the following sentences:

'My boundaries around my health and fitness are...'

'My boundaries around my finances are...'

'My boundaries around caring for my family are...'

'My boundaries around how I'm treated are...'

'My boundaries around time for me are...'

'My boundaries around romantic relationships are...'

'Having clear boundaries will enable me to achieve...'

An example of a romantic relationship boundary, to nurture and protect it, is saying to someone who's asked you to work late: 'I can't work tonight, it's our date night.'

> Your boundaries may be tested if others sense that you're not convinced of them. It's therefore important that you know why you've made them and what positive benefits they give you.

Most people will respect your boundaries. However, **Alpha people may push you to break them for the sake of their own agendas. With Alpha people, be concise and firm,** for example by saying: 'I can't work on Sunday's.'

If there's still push-back use the idea of having a rule and say: 'My rule is that I prioritise my family at weekends. I therefore don't work on Sundays.'

Your boundaries may be more fluid with those you love. This may be appropriate, or this can lead to you being disrespected if their agenda persistently trumps your own. If this is the case, monitor the dynamics of this relationship.

It can be a challenging thing to face, but you may need to start putting in firmer boundaries if your loved ones make unreasonable demands of you.

Boundaries have several benefits, and you may find that:

- Others show you greater respect for stating your needs

- They help you take care of yourself

- They help you to have time to meet your needs

- You teach others how you wish to be treated

- You show yourself respect

You may decide to be flexible about your boundaries as your needs change. You may, for example, decide not to stick to them in certain situations, such as an emergency. So long as you know your rationale for them, you can manage them appropriately.

⊘ Affirmation

> I show myself respect by setting boundaries with others.

How to use Affirmations: Repeat these in your head or out loud 5 times every morning when you get up and 5 times when you go to bed. You can also repeat them at times of stress. It may seem silly at first (!) but these ideas will start to embed in your mind over time.

 Tips from the Coach

- Boundaries enable you to direct energy to the areas of your life that are important to you

- Referring back to why you have boundaries means that you're more likely to keep them

- Most people will accept your boundaries but if you're pushed by a person who shows Alpha behaviour, hold your ground

- Boundaries can flex according to changing circumstances

💭 My Reflection

I could consider being clearer about my boundaries because...

Challenging behaviour: ways to respond to aggression from others

Experiencing unwelcome behaviour such as **micro aggressions**, can have a detrimental impact on your health and confidence. Microaggressions are slights, whether intentional or not, which communicate hostile attitudes to marginalised groups – such as people with a disability or to the elderly for example. You don't need to gloss over unwelcome behaviour from others - you've the right to be treated respectfully. The bottom line is, if other people's behaviour bothers you, you should - and can - address it.

It can be tempting to label someone a **bully**, but this is unhelpful. There are two reasons for this 1) it's difficult to prove and 2) nobody ever agrees that they're a bully! It may be more helpful to say that someone has **challenging behaviours**, which can't be disputed.

Your response to challenging behaviour should be proportionate. So, if you feel very intimidated, the response will be much stronger than if you're just irritated.

There are a variety of ways to address challenging behaviour such as: calling it out at the time, a clear conversation, setting a boundary (see Passivity 5), making a complaint, mediation, moving roles, leaving a workplace or relationship, taking legal action or involving the police.

In terms of calling out challenging behaviour, it would sound something like this: **'When you say 'X,' I find this disrespectful'**. It's useful to highlight challenging behaviour at the time, so that there's no ambiguity about the issue and when it happened.

A clear conversation is talking to the person privately about what bothers you, listening to their perspective and jointly deciding how to make positive change in the relationship. This needs to be carefully planned to ensure the best possible chance of a successful outcome.

With issues at work, HR can support and explain the relevant processes you may wish to consider. Workplace mediation is useful if a clear conversation with the person involved doesn't yield a positive change or isn't possible.

If the challenging behaviour is beyond what you're willing to tolerate and, particularly, if you feel intimidated or unsafe, you may wish to leave being with that person. Give no excuse – just go.

This is a complex area but whatever the circumstances, addressing challenging behaviour will be empowering for you.

 **Affirmation**

> **I always address disrespectful behaviour.**

How to use Affirmations: Repeat these in your head or out loud 5 times every morning when you get up and 5 times when you go to bed. You can also repeat them at times of stress. It may seem silly at first (!) but these ideas will start to embed in your mind over time.

My Reflection

I could consider addressing challenging behaviours because...

 Tips from the Coach

- You don't have to tolerate challenging behaviour towards you from anyone

- Knowing what tools you've at your disposal will give you the confidence to deal with any kind of disrespectful behaviour

Compliance: when to rebel

You may consider yourself to be a well-behaved person.
Of course, most of the time being compliant is appropriate.
Agreeing should, however, always be for the right reason
such as doing what's in your job description.

Sometimes you may have thoughts about how things could be
done differently – and better. Despite it not being your habit,
it's OK to challenge or disagree, especially if you feel strongly
about it. Not speaking up over an issue you feel is important
may cause you to feel disempowered.

**You may see challenge as being pushy and not being
a nice person. But the reality is that you can be
empowered and nice.** It just means that, from time-to-time,
you may need to flex yourself into a more assertive style of
communication.

You don't need to aggressively put your case. But addressing
the issue through explaining, listening, reflecting back and
negotiating is how you become more empowered.

An example of being both non-compliant and empowered would
be that you say to your line manager: 'I appreciate that you
want me to finish this project, but a secondment has come up
that's a great fit for my development. I'm going to apply for it
but I'm giving you a heads-up now so that you're aware. Can
we talk about this? I'd like to hear your view.'

Finding your inner rebel or, perhaps, your 'inner teenager'
(!) can help bring out the innate audaciousness you have
inside you.

Affirmation

> I can shake things up
> if I want to.

How to use Affirmations: Repeat these in your head or out loud 5 times every morning when you get up and 5 times when you go to bed. You can also repeat them at times of stress. It may seem silly at first (!) but these ideas will start to embed in your mind over time.

 Tips from the Coach

- You've the ability to stand up and be audacious if you want to

- Motivate yourself by remembering what you hope to achieve by not being compliant

💭 My Reflection

I could consider being less compliant because...

8 Confrontations: having clear conversations about sensitive subjects

You may consider that talking to another person about sensitive subjects, for example, their poor performance at work is very challenging.

You may think: 'I must confront 'X' with this...' And then, you may not do it because it feels too daunting. Or, if it does go ahead, you may find it awkward, negative and stressful. You may use written communication to make your points, rather than speak directly to the person involved - which may not land well.

In these situations, **it's helpful to reframe confrontations as clear conversations.** Think of a clear conversation as putting a subject in front of a person for discussion. Start off by talking about the problem but keep the momentum towards practical solutions, especially if you start to get bogged down in the issue. Allow time for you both to explore your perspectives. Ask questions, consider the answers you hear with curiosity. Calmly disagree and put your point of view if it's needed.

Your intent is crucial. You're here to try and resolve things, not to apportion blame. Blame will destroy trust and escalate things into a potential conflict.

> Go in with the mind-set that you don't know everything and want to understand.

State things positively, for example, instead of saying: 'I don't want to be in this role any longer' say: 'I've enjoyed this role and have learnt a lot but feel it's time for me to move on. Can we talk about this?'

Aim to end your clear conversation on a positive note by saying something like: 'I'm glad to have had this chance to talk to you' or 'I feel much better to have aired this – thank you for listening.'

You can't guarantee that the person you're talking to will want to explore things in an open, positive way too. They may shut down or get angry and defensive. In these circumstances, you could say: 'I can see that this isn't a good time for you right now. As far as I'm concerned, the door is always open if you'd like to talk at another time.'

Or you could just decide to move on from this issue, knowing that you've done all that you can.

 Affirmation

> **I can calmly explore issues with anyone.**

How to use Affirmations: Repeat these in your head or out loud 5 times every morning when you get up and 5 times when you go to bed. You can also repeat them at times of stress. It may seem silly at first (!) but these ideas will start to embed in your mind over time.

My Reflection

I could consider calling **'confrontations'** **'clear conversations'** because...

 Tips from the Coach

- Put a subject in front of someone for discussion rather than facing them with it

- When talking about a challenging subject, avoid blame

- Keep the momentum in a clear conversation heading towards a solution

⑨ Courage: finding your inner power

Even if you feel disadvantaged such as being disabled, lacking in education or experience, you've more power than you think.

You may have categorised yourself as a passive person. But, when you reflect on that, what's your proof? Is it possible that you're actually quietly assertive? You just may not be labelling your behaviour as empowered.

To see if this applies to you, consider completing the following sentences with examples from your past:

'I called someone out for poor behaviour when I…'

'I asked for what I needed when I…'

'I initiated communication with someone when I…'

'I made a difficult decision, which other people didn't expect, when I…'

'I've been vulnerable with others when I…'

'I stepped in publicly to help when I…'

'I turned someone down when I…'

If you think about it, you may have examples for some, even all, of these things. This is your proof that you've already been empowered and courageous.

Ask yourself: **'If I used my innate courage more, how could that change my life?'**

Your courage can be affected by your level of self-belief. If you feel that you would benefit from nurturing a positive relationship with yourself, then consider the: **Increasing Inner Confidence Workbook,** in the **Coaching Psychology Series.**

Affirmation

> **I'm courageous.**

How to use Affirmations: Repeat these in your head or out loud 5 times every morning when you get up and 5 times when you go to bed. You can also repeat them at times of stress. It may seem silly at first (!) but these ideas will start to embed in your mind over time.

 Tips from the Coach

- Your courageousness may be something that you've ignored
- It's a worthwhile exercise to prove to yourself, with evidence from your past, that you're much more empowered than you think

☁ **My Reflection**

I could consider using my innate courageousness more
because...

10 Initiating: actively pursuing your goals

It may not be your habit to initiate communication with people that you don't know. However, the act of initiating can open doors to new experiences, connections and opportunities to help you to achieve your goals. Initiating can be particularly useful at the start of a project or when you're considering an idea.

You may, for example, want to approach specialists, institutions, charities, groups and sponsors for information and support. Inevitably, not all of your approaches will bear fruit but by talking to new people, you'll learn and grow your network.

If there's more you want to get from your job, you could consider approaching Human Resources, your line manager or Directors and colleagues you don't know for support. Initiating communication at work might also include asking for coaching, mentoring, training or job shadowing so that you can get experience and clarify your needs.

> **You'll be thought of as driven and dynamic for having enthusiasm. This will be appreciated by others who are likely to then think of ways to support you.**

 Affirmation

> ## I'm proactive.

How to use Affirmations: Repeat these in your head or out loud 5 times every morning when you get up and 5 times when you go to bed. You can also repeat them at times of stress. It may seem silly at first (!) but these ideas will start to embed in your mind over time.

Tips from the Coach

- When you're in the early stages of an idea consider initiating communication with others to support you

- If you're enthusiastic people are more likely to get on board with your ideas

☁ **My Reflection**

I could consider initiating communication with others because...

Meetings: being more empowered when communicating in groups

You may find that dominant personalities take over meetings that you attend. You may feel that your input isn't encouraged or that expressing your views is challenging.

Speaking up in meetings is particularly important in the following situations:

- If you see poor behaviours from others

- If you want to be considered for a more senior position

- If you're in a senior position and are leading

- If you've something important to contribute

- If you've strong reasons to disagree with what's being said

Think about the purpose of your attendance in the meeting. Then make an effort to contribute to fulfil that purpose - despite more dominant personalities in the room. After all, you've just as much right to contribute as them. If there isn't a clear purpose for your attendance, then there's no need to be there.

If you witness poor behaviour in a meeting, see this as an opportunity to change the culture and empower yourself. Consider saying: 'When you just said <repeat back verbatim what was said> I felt uncomfortable. I don't know about anyone else, but I don't believe that this sort of language supports the culture of our organisation'.

If it's challenging to get your voice heard, let the louder attendees speak first to get what they want to say off their chest. Listen to the discussion, noting top-level points. When you feel that this is finished, summarise what you've heard and then give your view.

When preparing to speak, ask yourself: **'What's the most concise and persuasive way for me to explain this?'**

Bear in mind how this will land with others and ask yourself: **'How can I defend my view?'**

When you feel like you're going to sit back on something you want to say ask yourself: **'How frustrating will it be for me later not to have said this right now?'**

⊘ Affirmation

> **I say what needs to be said.**

How to use Affirmations: Repeat these in your head or out loud 5 times every morning when you get up and 5 times when you go to bed. You can also repeat them at times of stress. It may seem silly at first (!) but these ideas will start to embed in your mind over time.

My Reflection

I could consider contributing more to meetings because...

 Tips from the Coach

- If you don't contribute to meetings, question if you need to be there

- If you do need to be in a meeting, contribute your views, no matter what dynamics other people bring to the room

Needs and wants: deciding goals which give your life meaning

What you **need** is what gives your life fulfilment and happiness. What you **want** relates to what you would prefer to happen and items that you would like to own. Wants are things that, if you thought about it, you could compromise about.

It's time well spent to reflect on your needs and wants. Examples of your needs might be:

- Achieving positive change in your career

- Actively engaging with charitable work

- Caring for your family

- Driving your career

- Feeling autonomous

- Having intellectual challenge

- Having secure finances

- Having time to pursue your creativity and hobbies

- Practising your chosen spirituality or religion

- Prioritising your mental and physical health

- Spending time with close friends

After reflecting, if you're not sure about your needs and wants you may benefit from seeking support from a coach to help clarify this with you. Your goals are based on your needs. Your needs will change over time and so they'll need to be periodically reviewed.

Crucially, when thinking about where to spend your energy and time, this should be on your needs, not your wants.

Affirmation

> **I know what to prioritise.**

How to use Affirmations: Repeat these in your head or out loud 5 times every morning when you get up and 5 times when you go to bed. You can also repeat them at times of stress. It may seem silly at first (!) but these ideas will start to embed in your mind over time.

 Tips from the Coach

- Knowing your needs gives you a clear rationale of when to be persistent and set boundaries
- Empowerment is prioritising what's important to you

My Reflection

I could consider being clearer about my needs and wants because...

Positivity: managing negative biases

You may believe that actively pursuing your goals will ultimately cause you stress and challenge, which puts you off trying. There may be a defeatist element to your thinking where you feel that you've failed before you've even started.

These types of negative thoughts are barriers to you engaging with empowered behaviour. You may benefit from reasoning with them through an internal dialogue. This dialogue should balance the hypothetical downsides of action with potential benefits.

The truth is, you just don't know what the outcome will be, unless you try. Some of your negative thoughts may have a valid, logical basis. Yes, you may experience stress and challenge by becoming empowered. But it's equally true that there's stress and challenge being passive and not living the life that you deserve.

If you start to feel negative, ask yourself: **'What's the more positive interpretation of this situation?'**

Your mind is immensely powerful, but you've more control of it than you think. Positivity provides energy to fuel empowered behaviour.

Affirmation

> **I'm a powerhouse of positive energy.**

How to use Affirmations: Repeat these in your head or out loud 5 times every morning when you get up and 5 times when you go to bed. You can also repeat them at times of stress. It may seem silly at first (!) but these ideas will start to embed in your mind over time.

 Tips from the Coach

- Nourish yourself with positive thoughts about what empowered behaviour can bring to your life

- Consciously challenge negative thinking

- You've more control of your mind than you think

💭 **My Reflection**

I could consider being more positive because...

Potential: achieving whatever success means to you

Your skills are unique to you, whether they're practical, emotional, caring, scientific, sporting, adventurous, artistic, intellectual, academic, creative or musical etc. You may not even know what dormant skills you have, as they're yet to be explored.

> There may be some inner conflict around the sense of safety you feel with what you know and the more ambitious part of yourself that wants to develop. Aim to nurture that ambitious part.

If you've a sense of stagnation, you may have reached the limit of what your current situation can offer you in terms of development. This may lead to feelings of frustration or disappointment.

If this is the case, ask yourself: **'What do I have a thirst to explore?'** as this can give you a sense of where you would like to grow.

You may be using some of your skills in your current work situation but feel that there's more that you could do to develop. You may, for example, be interested in getting business skills to go self-employed, studying for an academic qualification, working overseas or learning a foreign language etc.

Affirmation

> **I commit to living my life to its fullest potential.**

How to use Affirmations: Repeat these in your head or out loud 5 times every morning when you get up and 5 times when you go to bed. You can also repeat them at times of stress. It may seem silly at first (!) but these ideas will start to embed in your mind over time.

 ## Tips from the Coach

- A passive approach to development can only lead to you feeling unfulfilled

- If you feel stagnated in terms of your development, it's time to consider other options

- You may only be using certain parts of your skillset. It's likely that you've many other abilities that you've yet to explore

My Reflection

I could consider how to reach my full potential because...

Resilience: staying persistent and flexible

Your attitude to life events, such as being turned down for a job interview, for example, is vitally important. You may shrink back into passivity after a disappointment – but don't give up hope. This doesn't have to be the only chance to get your needs met. Resilience is about staying flexible in the face of challenges.

Consider using persistence as a tactic to increase your resilience. In the case of your career, tell yourself: 'this organisation has rejected me on this occasion but I'm not going to give up on getting another role in the future'.

Despite setbacks, rather than getting disappointed, be more accepting. A rejection, say, isn't necessarily the end of the road for achieving your goal. It could just be a step in the process of achieving it in a different way.

 Affirmation

> **I'm persistent and accepting.**

How to use Affirmations: Repeat these in your head or out loud 5 times every morning when you get up and 5 times when you go to bed. You can also repeat them at times of stress. It may seem silly at first (!) but these ideas will start to embed in your mind over time.

My Reflection

I could consider being more resilient because...

 Tips from the Coach

- Being flexible and accepting will enable you to keep striving for what you want

- Passivity holds you back, persistence drives you forward

16 Responsibility: being accountable for yourself

You may feel that others have taken charge of certain aspects of your life in the past. You may, for example, have been encouraged into your particular career - even though it wasn't your choice. In fact, you might just be drifting along not making many decisions for yourself.

If these decisions don't sit well with you, there are likely to be some knock-on emotional issues such as: inner conflict, depression, resentment and frustration about not expressing yourself or being more in control.

> It may be time to talk to the person who has been doing the heavy lifting in your life. You've the opportunity to explain that they can now relinquish control as you'll start to assert your authority over yourself.

You may, for example, want to consider a new career or explore other avenues across a range of areas in your life.

Taking more responsibility for your own decisions means putting more effort into living a life where you feel more authentically you. **Whether your decisions turn out well, or even if they're mistakes, they're your own. And you can learn from them.**

This may seem selfish and confusing to others, as they will need to adjust to the new you and the changes you're making.

It may also lead to repercussions that you can't control. Some people will accept these changes, but others may want you to stay the person they felt comfortable with.

As challenging as their reaction may be, staying dependent will be unhelpful to you in the long-term.

Aim to be as compassionate and honest as you can be with your loved ones, recognising that change may not be easy for anyone, including you.

However, the long-term benefits of self-belief and emotional harmony are worth it.

✓ Affirmation

I'm in charge of me.

How to use Affirmations: Repeat these in your head or out loud 5 times every morning when you get up and 5 times when you go to bed. You can also repeat them at times of stress. It may seem silly at first (!) but these ideas will start to embed in your mind over time.

Tips from the Coach

- It will feel powerful to lead on the decisions you make for yourself

- Although it might cause others to have to make adjustments, in the long-term taking responsibility will enable you to truly be yourself

💭 My Reflection

I could consider taking more responsibility for myself because...

Role-plays: practicing communicating before a live event

A way to practice how to communicate – perhaps with more challenging situations that are coming up – is with a role-play. This doesn't have to be in a group setting, it could just be with a trusted friend or coach.

> Role-plays can be helpful if you're not sure how to position what you want to say and also if you want to try out some techniques.

Ask your friend or coach to play the part of the person you intend to speak to. Ask them to behave like them. Make it as realistic as possible by briefing them about the situation and the personality of the person you intend to communicate with. Act in the role-play as you would do in the actual event.

Afterwards, ask your friend or coach for feedback. Focus on whether the way you communicated was effective and what you could do better.

Conversations are dynamic and scripts aren't possible, but trying out your skills will help you to be more practiced when the time comes.

Affirmation

> **Role plays are fun and useful.**

How to use Affirmations: Repeat these in your head or out loud 5 times every morning when you get up and 5 times when you go to bed. You can also repeat them at times of stress. It may seem silly at first (!) but these ideas will start to embed in your mind over time.

 Tips from the Coach

- Role-plays are like an icebreaker in advance of a future conversation that you might feel uncertain about

- Treat role-plays like a simulation where you can safely try out communication tools

☁ **My Reflection**

I could consider using role-plays because...

Saying 'No': how to turn someone down

If someone makes a request of you, you may find it challenging to turn them down. You may even have a **reflex Yes.** This 'Yes' response may mean that you get overwhelmed with commitments.

You've a right to turn people down, it doesn't mean that you're selfish or uncaring. It's just that from time-to-time you've got other priorities.

Some thoughts about saying 'No' are:

- Don't assume that it's a big deal for the other person to be turned down, they may already have a Plan B, for example, another person that they could ask

- Every 'Yes' you say means giving time and energy to that activity - so be careful about committing

- If the requester cares about you, they'll understand why it's not possible and not be resentful

- It's better to say 'No' when you're first approached, than to 'reflex Yes' and potentially have to let someone down later

- Saying 'No' doesn't mean that you're inadequate, it just means that you're prioritising

- Saying 'Yes' to too many requests will always cause you stress

- You've the right to say 'No,' even if there's a power imbalance (such as between you and your line manager) if you've a justification

In terms of how to politely say 'No,' consider starting with gratitude, for example: **'I'm grateful that you've thought of me but I'm afraid I can't'.**

If you want to explain your regret, say: **'I'm grateful that you've thought of me, and I feel regret about this but I'm afraid I can't'.**

If you can think of someone else who can help, suggest it. Be as honest as you feel comfortable - except if the requester shows Alpha behaviour. In this situation, if you launch into excuses, they may try to find solutions to change your mind. In this scenario shut the conversation down and say: **'Let me put it another way, I've a rule that I must prioritise my family'.**

Don't apologise for turning someone down. You only need to apologise when you've done something you shouldn't have, or if you've failed to do something that you should.

Aim to leave things on a good note; but if the person is grumpy, that's OK too. You can't please everyone. If you've a strong rationale for turning someone down, then there's no need to feel guilty.

 **Affirmation**

My needs are important.

How to use Affirmations: Repeat these in your head or out loud 5 times every morning when you get up and 5 times when you go to bed. You can also repeat them at times of stress. It may seem silly at first (!) but these ideas will start to embed in your mind over time.

☁ My Reflection

I could consider saying 'No' more because...

Tips from the Coach

- Reflect before you commit yourself

- With people who have a tendency towards Alpha behaviour, be more direct when you turn them down

- Explain why you can't do something, but don't apologise

19 Saying 'Yes': agreeing to something assertively

You may think: 'I don't have a problem with saying 'Yes' - I do it all the time!' However, let's consider how you say 'Yes'.

Ask yourself: **'Do I investigate requests thoroughly before I agree to them?'**

If you don't, then you may benefit from probing into exactly what's expected of you, by asking questions.

If the requester isn't clear what the scope is, then say: 'I need to be clearer about this before I can decide. Please could you get back to me when you know more?'

> Be cautious about a belief that the future is going to have more available time than the present. This belief can lead you to commit yourself to future activities when there's no guarantee it will be any less busy then.

Once you're clear about the request, ask yourself: **'To what extent can I commit?'**

Be specific with the requester when you respond, for example, say: 'I can project manage this for the next six weeks and then I'm on holiday'. Or 'I can carpool on Tuesdays, but I'll have to review this in the Autumn'.

You might also want to add caveats, for example: '...three times a month I can't do this because I've family commitments'.

In other words, your 'Yes' may have its own set of boundaries.

If you're not clear about what you can commit to, say: 'I'll get back to you with an answer'. This gives you time to reflect and decide what you can commit to.

⊘ Affirmation

> **I'm thoughtful about what I commit to.**

How to use Affirmations: Repeat these in your head or out loud 5 times every morning when you get up and 5 times when you go to bed. You can also repeat them at times of stress. It may seem silly at first (!) but these ideas will start to embed in your mind over time.

 Tips from the Coach

- In order to manage other people's expectations and your own stress levels, analyse every request that's made of you before you agree to it

- There's no guarantee that you'll have more time available in the future, so be careful of obligations you agree to

☁ **My Reflection**

I could consider being clearer when I say 'Yes' because...

20 Self-deprecation: avoiding being over-modest

You may tend to down-grade your abilities when you describe yourself to others.

Don't bad mouth yourself, under any circumstances! If you're tempted to say: 'I'm hopeless at that' or 'you're great at this, but I'm hopeless at it' stop yourself. You don't have to put yourself down to praise others.

If someone praises you, say: 'I really appreciate that' not 'you didn't have to say that' or 'you shouldn't have, it was nothing'. **People don't give praise for no reason.** Instead, consider what you're being praised for and mentally note this as one of your strengths.

Be realistic about your skill set. You don't have to say that you can run a marathon when you can't! Present a lack of skill neutrally and factually, rather than as a personal failure, for example, just simply say: 'I don't run marathons'.

Others will recognise your own self-evaluation. You may have strong inner confidence but if you downgrade yourself to others, they'll assume that you don't. This is confusing and not helpful to you.

Affirmation

> ## I have my own back.

How to use Affirmations: Repeat these in your head or out loud 5 times every morning when you get up and 5 times when you go to bed. You can also repeat them at times of stress. It may seem silly at first (!) but these ideas will start to embed in your mind over time.

 Tips from the Coach

- Express respect for yourself in the way that you talk about yourself to others

- Be honest about your skills and factual about your shortcomings

💭 **My Reflection**

I could consider being less self-deprecating because...

21 Therapy: considering the roots of your behaviour

It can be useful to explore why you behave as you do with a professional counsellor or therapist. This is particularly important if you find managing your emotions is challenging or if you've experienced trauma. Having insight into yourself, means that you'll find it easier to develop empowered behaviours because you'll build on a strong knowledgebase.

You may have copied Alpha behaviour patterns from role models in your past, such as parents/caregivers, which may not be helpful to you. You may also be automatically reacting to situations based on protective emotional patterns you've developed from your past.

Your workplace may offer access to confidential counselling services which can be a useful resource. GPs may also have counselling services you can access. Private counsellors are also available face-to-face, online and on the phone. Some professional memberships also offer counselling.

You could also consider hypnotherapy, which works through deep relaxation to positively influence you at a sub-conscious level. This is particularly useful to remove unhelpful subconscious behaviour patterns.

In all cases, work with a therapist who has been professionally trained and is registered with an approved body.

Affirmation

> **I'm open to exploring my inner self with a therapist.**

How to use Affirmations: Repeat these in your head or out loud 5 times every morning when you get up and 5 times when you go to bed. You can also repeat them at times of stress. It may seem silly at first (!) but these ideas will start to embed in your mind over time.

 Tips from the Coach

- Therapy can give you clarity about why you behave in the way that you do

- Hypnotherapy can work at a sub-conscious level to free you from unhelpful automatic behaviour patterns

My Reflection

I could consider therapy because...

Time: managing people who steal your time

You may not pay much attention to how you're using your time. As a consequence, it may be bleeding into other people's agendas. You may also be interrupted with calls, emails or by giving advice and emotional support. As helpful as this may be to others, being everything to everyone may mean that you push your needs to the bottom of the list.

> **To clarify your thoughts around how you spend your time, ask yourself:**
>
> 'Who takes my time?'
>
> 'Why do they take my time?'
>
> 'How do they take my time?'
>
> 'Do I need to protect my time to meet my needs?'
>
> 'How can I protect my time?'
>
> 'Is a clear conversation about my time needed?'

If you've an open-door policy and your mobile and other communication channels are constantly switched on, then this indicates to others that you're available for them.

Supporting other people is admirable but there should be a balance between meeting your own needs and meeting theirs.

Consider when to close doors and mute electronic systems to protect your time. Be specific and let people know when it's convenient to be interrupted – and, crucially, when it's not. When someone regularly interrupts you either ignore it or consider saying: 'I'm busy now'. If you want to see them when you're ready, say: 'Let's arrange another time'.

Use your email 'out of office' function to politely explain your boundaries such as: 'Thanks for emailing. I don't work after 5:30 pm. I'll pick this up with you tomorrow'.

 Affirmation

> **I spend my time to create the greatest benefits in my life.**

How to use Affirmations: Repeat these in your head or out loud 5 times every morning when you get up and 5 times when you go to bed. You can also repeat them at times of stress. It may seem silly at first (!) but these ideas will start to embed in your mind over time.

 Tips from the Coach

- Treat spending time like spending money. It's not a limitless pool you can keep drawing from

- Spend your time to meet your needs

☁ **My Reflection**

I could consider how to protect my time because...

Time to think: giving yourself space to decide the smartest course of action

Sometimes you'll just need more time to consider something before acting. **Others might put pressure on you to decide but who needs an immediate response?** Rarely is this necessary, except perhaps in an emergency.

If you're considering making changes to your life, you may need reflection time. So, consider, for example, saying to a recruiter: 'I need more time to think about this job offer'. This type of response will be satisfactory for most reasonable people. In fact, they're likely to respect you for giving it serious consideration.

It may be helpful to negotiate the time that you need, for example, by saying: 'I'm interested, but before I commit, give me 24 hours to make my decision'. An alternative would be: 'I need to give this more thought and I'd like to get back to you first thing on Monday morning with my answer'.

Take the pressure off yourself and give yourself the space to consider the pros and cons. Perhaps discuss implications with the people your decision affects. During your reflection, analyse your needs in relation to the situation. You may realise that you need further information to fully understand what's involved. Ask for that and for more time, if it's crucial for your decision.

Even though there's always uncertainty in every decision you make, careful reflection means that you're much more likely to make the right one.

However, for something that you know that you'll accept, be less cautious in your approach. Say 'Yes' and then work out the details later.

Affirmation

> **Sometimes people can wait for me to decide.**

How to use Affirmations: Repeat these in your head or out loud 5 times every morning when you get up and 5 times when you go to bed. You can also repeat them at times of stress. It may seem silly at first (!) but these ideas will start to embed in your mind over time.

 Tips from the Coach

- Nobody needs an immediate answer unless it's an emergency

- If you need to take time to consider your decision, do it - despite any pressure other people may be applying to get an answer

☁ **My Reflection**

I could consider giving myself more time to think because...

24 Vulnerability: being open about your needs and feelings

A carer who wrote a book about the regrets of the dying people she cared for[2] found that some wished they'd opened up more about what they felt to others. Being empowered is about opening up to others when you need to.

> If you're not used to articulating your needs and feelings, it may be daunting. However, there are ways to open up about more sensitive topics.

Be mindful about where you hold the conversation, for example, make sure it's private and that you've got plenty of time.

Consider framing an issue with depression, for example, like this: 'I haven't spoken about this before, but I need to tell you that depression has been a problem for me for several years and it's starting to affect my work'.

You may also want to honestly show your appreciation to a valued colleague, for example by saying: 'That was a challenging situation, which you managed very sensitively. Bob, you do a fantastic job and I feel honoured to have you on the team'.

When you get into the habit of more openly explaining your thoughts and feelings, it's likely that you'll foster connections with others. However, you may also feel a **vulnerability hangover**. This is where you reflect on what you've said and later feel uncomfortable.

---

[2] Ware, B. (2012) *The Top Five Regrets of the Dying* Hay House

Wait. Judge the effectiveness of your approach by how the situation develops, **not** by the discomfort you feel afterwards. A vulnerability hangover is actually evidence of you successfully being authentically yourself to others. What can be more powerful than that?

 Affirmation

> **I show respect towards my needs and feelings by expressing them.**

How to use Affirmations: Repeat these in your head or out loud 5 times every morning when you get up and 5 times when you go to bed. You can also repeat them at times of stress. It may seem silly at first (!) but these ideas will start to embed in your mind over time.

 Tips from the Coach

- Being open is a powerful way to be understood
- Honestly articulating your needs can support you with managing your stress

💭 **My Reflection**

I could consider opening up about my needs and feelings because...

25 Your voice: using your voice more

There'll always be a route to express yourself, whether that's physically through your voice or the written word.

To encourage your voice, start by vocalising your needs in the mirror. You might, for example, say: 'I'm ready for promotion'.

You could then consider saying this to others – and then, for example, at an interview.

> Affirmations which are included throughout this Workbook empower your voice. You could choose one and say this loudly, for example, when you're in the shower.

You can also strengthen your voice by singing, if that seems fun to you (it doesn't matter whether you're in tune or not!).

If your speech is quiet, then up the volume.

When you speak, avoid passive expressions such as: 'it's up to you,' 'I don't mind' or 'whatever you want'. Replace these with more energetic phrases such as: 'my view is,' 'I think this approach would work' or 'I'd like to add...'

> Avoid relying on the written word rather than communicating face-to-face. Complex situations are much more effectively addressed when you speak.

If you've a disability, you could use your voice through another communication method such as sign language or a computer. Whatever tool you have to hand, **use your voice to empower yourself.**

Affirmation

> ## I have a strong voice.

How to use Affirmations: Repeat these in your head or out loud 5 times every morning when you get up and 5 times when you go to bed. You can also repeat them at times of stress. It may seem silly at first (!) but these ideas will start to embed in your mind over time.

 ## Tips from the Coach

- You can use your voice to express yourself
- Use all tools at hand to communicate your way out of passivity

☁ **My Reflection**

I could consider encouraging my voice because...

Goal setting

Take time to note your thoughts and plans relating to becoming empowered.

Ask yourself: **'How will I reward myself for working on this?'**

1	
2	
3	
4	
5	

Empowerment Audit

The purpose of this audit is to analyse what type of behaviour you tend to use. It's a bit of fun to get a feel for what your tendency is.

You may not need to do this if you've already taken a psychometric assessment which measures 'assertiveness' (such as NEO-PI-3 or EQi).

Please choose one of the three answers that's closest to your likely response.

1 **You would prefer to go abroad on holiday with just your partner. However, your partner wants to bring their parents too.**

Do you:

a) Go with your partner and your partner's family, to keep the peace.

b) Say how you feel and what you would like - negotiate with your partner.

c) Flatly refuse to go if your partner's parents are coming.

You've just started your main course in a restaurant. It should be hot but it's tepid.

Do you:

a) Eat it anyway (or at least try to) even though it's unappetising. Certainly don't complain.

b) Tell the waiter it's tepid and ask for a replacement at the right temperature.

c) Point out to the waiter that this isn't good enough and say that if another meal isn't immediately produced, you'll complain about the restaurant on social media.

3 **A colleague keeps inviting you to join a dinner party circle. You've other friends and want to use your time in other ways.**

Do you:

a) Go to the dinner parties anyway and host some yourself, even though you don't enjoy it.

b) Say that dinner parties aren't really your thing but thank your colleague for their invitation.

c) Tell your colleague that you don't see the point.

4 You're on an interview panel as a recruiter and one of the panel members wants to ask a question that seems sexist to you. You're concerned.

Do you:

a) Do nothing so that the question stays in, despite your concerns.

b) Politely explain your concerns with your co-panel member.

c) Point out how wrong the question is and lecture your colleague on bias.

5 When you're in a car park, another car takes the space that you've clearly been waiting for.

Do you:

a) Back off at once and let them take the space.

b) Let it go, find another space and think **'that's how some people are'.**

c) Seek out the driver that took 'your' place after you've parked elsewhere and tell them that their behaviour was selfish.

6 **Someone scoffs at an award you've received at work, which you find undermining.**

Do you:

a) Say nothing but feel upset and undermined by their behaviour.

b) Take the person aside, say that you felt upset by their remarks. Ask them what was going through their mind when they referred to your award in that way.

c) Publicly tell that person that they're out of order and ask them what their problem is.

7 **You're asked to work late for the third time in a week, as a favour to your line manager. You've another appointment that evening though.**

Do you:

a) Cancel your appointment, for an easy life.

b) Early on, explain to your line manager that you can't do three evenings overtime in a row, and that tonight you've another appointment.

c) Just go to your appointment. You don't have to explain anything to anyone.

8 **Your family don't seem to be listening to you when you try telling them about a club you've joined, that you're excited about.**

Do you:

a) Keep quiet – what you do is clearly not important to them.

b) Ask for their attention, share your excitement with them and explain why this is important to you.

c) Accuse everyone of ignoring you and not caring. Then go off and sulk.

9 **Your line manager keeps giving you more work. You've absorbed as much as you can, but your stress levels are getting high. You're concerned about burning out.**

Do you:

a) Suffer in silence.

b) Explain to your line manager how you feel and what's possible for you in the allotted time. Discuss priorities with them and explain what you need to protect your health.

c) Tell your boss what you will and won't do. Give curt responses to them from then on and undermine them at every opportunity, both to their face and behind their back. Bear a grudge.

Your beloved pet has just died. You're struggling with the trauma of their loss at work.

Do you:

a) Hide what you're feeling, after all, they were just a pet.

b) Confide in your manager/a colleague about how sad you're feeling so that they understand and can give you emotional support.

c) Be in a bad mood with everybody but don't explain why.

Mostly A's

Your behaviour tends to be passive.

Mostly B's

Your behaviour tends to be empowered.

Mostly C's

Your behaviour tends to be Alpha.

🖊 Notes to Coaches

This section provides approaches for incorporating the Workbooks into your current practice as a tool.

The psychological theories, ideas and approaches the Workbooks draw on are: attachment theory, cognitive behavioural therapy/coaching, deliberate practice, free trait theory, hypnotherapy, learning styles, logotherapy, naïve realism, neuro-linguistic programming, neuroplasticity, positive psychology, psychoanalysis, rational emotive theory, spectrum hypothesis and transactional analysis.

When your client is aware of what area they wish to focus on in terms of self-development, but lack ideas about how to go about this, the Workbooks are an ideas bank for them.

As change is based on your client having the confidence to act, consider suggesting the **Increasing Inner Confidence Workbook** to them first.

Consider any neurodiversity your client may have. The Workbooks have a dyslexia friendly font and style. However, you may wish to consider highlighting areas for them to focus on if reading is challenging for them.

If your client has issues with frustration and anger, introduce the **Managing Emotions Workbook: Including Stress and Anger** first. The rationale is that they begin with strategies to manage themselves before they start to rethink their communication with the **Increasing Empowerment Workbook.**

The Workbooks can be used in conjunction with big five psychometric assessments, including NEO-PI-3.

The **Increasing Empowerment Workbook** can be used to support the assertiveness facet.

The **Increasing Inner Confidence Workbook** can be used to support the self-belief facet.

The **Managing Self-consciousness Workbook** can be used to support the self-consciousness facet.

The **Managing Emotions Workbook: Including Stress and Anger** can be used to support the openness to emotions, anger and vulnerability facets.

> **And, finally, expect the unexpected - your client may find surprising parts of the Workbooks influence their thinking!**

Top 10 Recommended Resources

1 Babcock, L. and Laschever, S. (2003) *Women Don't Ask: Negotiation and the Gender Divide* Princeton University Press

2 Back, K. & Back, K. (2005) *Assertiveness at Work: A Practical Guide to Handling Awkward Situations* (third edition) McGraw Hill

3 Berne, E. (1964) *Games People Play: The Psychology of Human Relationships* Penguin

4 Bunghay Stainer, M. (2016) *The Coaching Habit: Say Less, Ask More and Change the Way You Lead* Forever Page Two Books

5 Dickson, A. (2012) *A Woman in Your Own Right Assertiveness and You* Quartet Books Ltd

6 O'Connor, J. and Seymour, J. (1995) *Introducing NLP (Neuro-linguistic programming): Psychological Skills for Understanding and Influencing People* Revised edition. Thorsons

7 Stone, D., Patton B., Heen, S. (1999) *Difficult Conversations: How to Discuss What Matters Most* Penguin

8 Ware, B. (2012) *The Top Five Regrets of the Dying* Hay House

9 Willis, L. and Daisley, J. (1990) *Springboard Women's Development Workbook* (2013 Edition) Hawthorn Press

10 Stachowiak, D. (2023) How to Handle Pushback from Difficult Askers with Vaness Patrick *Coaching for Leaders* (Podcast) 23rd June 2023 available at https://coachingforleaders.com/

Final Thoughts

Return to this Workbook when you need to increase your empowerment, if you feel that you need a boost or reminder.

There's no 'done' - we're all a work in progress.

Set and keep daily habits to power change.

You can cope with anything that comes your way.

You've got this.

Notes